Making Meaning for Operations

In the Domains of Whole Numbers and Fractions

Casebook Supplement

by

Deborah Schifter
Virginia Bastable
Susan Jo Russell

Boston, Massachusetts • Chandler, Arizona • Glenview, Illinois • Upper Saddle River, New Jersey

ISBN 13: 978-0-13-373314-3

ISBN 10:   0-13-373314-9

1 2 3 4 5 6 7 8 9 10 V031 13 12 11 10 09

TEACHER COLLABORATORS   Allan Arnaboldi, Audrey Barzey, Nancy Buell, Rose Christiansen, Lisette Colon, Francis Cooper, Marcia Estelle, Victoria Fink, Christopher Fraley, Marta Garcia, Gail Gilmore, Scott Hendrickson, Nancy Horowitz, Kirsten Lee Howard, Bruce Kamerer, Robin Musser, Mark Paige, Angela Philactos, Margaret Riddle, Nicole Rigelman, Jan Rook, Sherry Sadjak, Karen Schweitzer, Malia Scott, Lisa Seyferth, Elizabeth Sweeney, Polly Wagner, Carol Walker, Steve Walkowicz, Dee Watson representing the public schools of Amherst (MA), Belchertown (MA), Bismarck (ND), Boston (MA), Brookline (MA), Buncomb County (NC), Newton (MA), Northampton (MA), Springfield (MA), Westfield (MA), Williamsburg (MA) and the Atrium School (MA), Brigham Young University (UT), and Portland State University (OR)

REVIEWERS AND CONSULTANTS   Tami Bird (Jordan Public Schools, UT), Thomas Carpenter (University of Wisconsin), Susan Empson (University of Texas), Benjamin Ford (Sonoma State University, CA), Sterling Hilton (Brigham Young University, UT), Barbara Kuehl (Salt Lake City Public Schools), Jill Bodner Lester (Mount Holyoke College), James Lewis (University of Nebraska), Amy Morse (Education Development Center), Katie Rafferty (Houston Independent School District), Sherry Sajdak (Boston Public Schools), Susan Bush Smith (Springfield Public Schools), Vicki Smith (Salt Lake City Public Schools), Virginia Stimpson (University of Washington), Joy Whitenack (Virginia Commonwealth University), Lisa Yaffee (independent consultant)

PROJECT EDITOR: Beverly Cory

DVD DEVELOPMENT   David Smith (David Smith Productions)

This work was supported by the National Science Foundation under Grant Nos. ESI-9254393 (awarded to EDC), ESI-0095450 (awarded to TERC), and ESI-0242609 (awarded to EDC). Any opinions, findings, conclusions, or recommendations expressed here are those of the authors and do not necessarily reflect the views of the National Science Foundation.

Additional support was provided by the ExxonMobil Foundation.

C O N T E N T S

Introduction   1

Chapter 1   Making meaning for whole-number addition and subtraction   5

CASE   1   Insects, spiders and counting on   7

       2   Going up and down with numbers   10

       3   Complexities of counting back   12

       4   Missing part versus missing change   15

       5   Valentine stickers   16

       6   Finding the difference: Should I add or subtract?   21

       7   Number line models for subtraction   30

Chapter 2   Making meaning for multiplication and division   35

CASE   8   Bunnies and eggs   36

       9   Early multiplication   42

       10   Candy canes in packages   46

       11   How do kids think about division?   48

       12   Are these kids or seeds?   51

Chapter 3   When dividing doesn't come out evenly   57

CASE   13   Can you divide 39 into 5?   58

       14   Can you divide 39 into 5? revisited   61

       15   7 Brownies, 4 people   67

       16   Zero is special; zero is nothing   70

Chapter 4   Greater than, less than, equal to   77

C A S E   17   Which is greater? How do you know?   78

18   Discovering common denominators   82

19   Equivalent fractions   87

20   Today's number is 1   88

21   Fraction flags   91

Chapter 5   Combining shares, or adding fractions   97

C A S E   22   Sharing brownies or adding fractions   98

23   How many ways can you add 1/3 to 1/4, or interesting
          stuff happens!   108

24   "Doling out" and fractions   111

Chapter 6   Taking portions of portions, or multiplying fractions   117

C A S E   25   Clock faces and equivalence   118

26   Multiplication of mixed numbers   120

27   What I want my students to understand about multiplication   125

Chapter 7   Expanding ideas about division in the context of fractions   129

C A S E   28   Who says that's not the right equation?
          My own experience vs. students' thinking   130

29   Stretching elastic   133

Chapter 8   Highlights of related research *by Lisa Yaffee*   **137**

S E C T I O N   1   Modeling addition and subtraction   138

2   Numerical reasoning begins   141

3   Modeling multiplication and division   143

4   Making meaning for multiplication and division   148

5   Encountering fractions in sharing situations   151

6   Understanding fractional amounts   156

7   Revising ideas for operations with fractions   162

Introduction

The cases in *Making Meaning for Operations* concentrate on such questions as these: What kinds of actions and situations are modeled by addition, subtraction, multiplication, and division? How do students, as they work with such situations, come to understand the operations? One seminar facilitator put it this way: "*Making Meaning for Operations* challenges our definition of *operation*. It brings operation out of a computation framework into a 'meaning' framework."

The casebook begins with a look at young children's counting strategies as they address problems which they will later solve by adding and subtracting. Chapters 1 and 2 examine the different types of situations that are modeled by whole-number addition/subtraction and multiplication/division. But as illustrated by the cases in chapter 3, the operation of division introduces a new kind of number, fractions, when the division doesn't come out evenly. Chapter 4 concentrates on how the numerator and denominator of a fraction together determine the size of the fraction.

The latter part of the casebook, chapters 5–7, revisits the operations in the context of fractions. What whole-number ideas, issues, and generalizations need to be refined or revised once the work is extended to include fractions? For example, how do you make sense of multiplying when the numbers being multiplied create a product smaller than you started with?

The cases are all written by elementary and middle school teachers, describing events from their own classrooms. The teacher-authors themselves are inquiring into how their students come to make meaning for operations. Writing these cases is part of that process of inquiry, and the teachers come together on a regular basis to read and discuss one another's work.

The casebook concludes with a chapter called "Highlights of Related Research." This essay summarizes some recent research findings that touch on the issues explored in the cases of *Making Meaning for Operations*.

When this DMI seminar was first taught, many seminar participants reported that they had to learn how to read the cases.

> It's different from reading a story. I feel as if I've had to comb through each episode with a fine-toothed comb.

> I'm reading cases very slowly, and I'm writing down thoughts about what I'm seeing in the text.

> I find that when I do the same mathematics problems the students in the case are working on, I can better understand what they are doing.

Several teachers offered advice to other participants:

> Read all the cases in a chapter once and try to write down the mathematical issues they raise. You might focus attention on two or three children that interest you and really figure out the mathematical issues that these few children are facing. Try to really understand how the children are thinking. Here's another way to do it: After reading all the cases in a chapter, go over them again, looking for common threads. What mathematical issues connect these cases together?

> Remember that these are glimpses of *real* kids dealing with *real* situations, struggling to make sense of very difficult concepts. Pay particular attention to the *natural* ways students often solve problems.

> Begin with the chapter introduction, which alerts you to the ideas you should pay attention to.

If possible, discuss the cases informally with other participants before the sessions. If you're unable to do any or some of the above, by all means don't *not* come to the seminar!

As the seminar proceeds, you might talk to other participants about the ways they read the cases to prepare for seminar discussions.

C H A P T E R

1

Making meaning for whole-number addition and subtraction

Case 1	Insects and spiders and counting on	*Dan, Grade 1, September*
Case 2	Going up and down with numbers	*Wendy, Kindergarten, March*
Case 3	Complexities of counting back	*Denise, Grade 2, October*
Case 4	Missing part versus missing change	*Kina, Grade 1, January*
Case 5	Valentine stickers	*Jody, Grades 1 and 2, January*
Case 6	Finding the difference: Should I add or subtract?	*Machiko, Grade 4, November*
Case 7	Number line models for subtraction	*Carl, Grade 7, June*

As you read the following word problems, consider for a moment which of the operations—addition, subtraction, multiplication, or division—you would use to find the answer to each one.

There are 13 insects on the paper in front of us and 5 spiders behind my back. What is the total number of insects and spiders?

There are 10 girls in our class, and 8 of them are here today. How many girls are out today?

We can easily identify the operations that would give us the answers: addition ($13 + 5 = 18$) and subtraction ($10 - 8 = 2$). But what is it that children must understand to solve these story problems? What happens when such problems are posed to children who have not yet learned symbols for the operations and have not yet learned their arithmetic facts? How do children find answers to such problems when they haven't yet learned to add or subtract? The first three cases of this chapter allow us to examine these questions. As you read these cases, take notes on these questions:

- While following the counting strategies that young children use to solve problems, and by pondering the confusions that arise for them, what do *we* learn about the operations?

- What do we learn about the ideas that children must put together in order for *them* to develop an understanding of the operations?

In the remaining cases in this chapter (cases 4–7), we meet students who have developed some ideas about addition and subtraction and can solve problems using these operations. However, the questions they ask, the confusions they hold, and the insights they offer reveal greater complexity underneath what may seem to be very basic concepts. One set of questions involves mathematical issues for ourselves:

- Can a single situation be modeled by different operations?

- Can a single operation model different kinds of actions?

- What can we see about the operations through different representations (cubes, number lines)?

A second set of questions prompts us to consider the children's processes of putting ideas together:

- In these samples from grades 1–7, what can we observe about the ways in which students' ideas develop?

- What appear to be some of the difficulties students face as they learn about addition and subtraction?

- How can different representations support students' understanding of addition and subtraction?

As you read the cases, take notes on these questions. Then, after reading the cases, review the questions again.

Insects and spiders and counting on

Dan

GRADE 1, SEPTEMBER

As part of our science study of insects and spiders, the children sorted small plastic models onto two large sheets of paper labeled *Insects* and *Spiders*. As they placed their models, they had to tell what attributes they were using to make their decisions. The following activity was an integration of math with this science study. After we sorted the models and confirmed that each was in the correct set, I asked, "How many insects are there?" | 5

The insects were positioned randomly on the sheet. I called on Mike. As he counted the insects, his finger jumped around from one to another, making it difficult to keep track of which ones he had counted and which | 10
he had missed. He ended up miscounting by 1, coming up with 14. Some children said they disagreed with his count.

I next asked Annie to count the insects. Although she didn't count them in an easily discernible order (e.g., left to right, or top to bottom, or by moving them as she counted), she was clearly able to keep track, since | 15
she did not recount or leave out any insects. She came up with the correct answer of 13.

I asked one more child, Renaldo, to count to see whether his answer would agree with either of the previous answers or would be completely different. He counted the insects in an organized way; as he said each | 20
number, he moved one item into a group of already counted insects. He came up with 13, just as Annie did.

I asked the group, "Why did we get different answers, 14 and 13?" Renaldo quickly replied that Mike had "counted too many." Nods from many of the children seemed to suggest agreement. I think he meant | 25
that Mike had counted some insect or insects more than once. Since the

Dan

children seemed content with Renaldo's response, I assumed they agreed that 13 was the answer and did not pursue this question any further.

The children were quickly able to see that there were only 5 spiders on the other sheet. Since we had not counted the total number of insects and spiders, I decided to find out how the children would determine how many there were altogether if I removed the 5 spiders from view. How would they solve the problem? How would they represent items that were absent and keep them in the count? Would they start at 13 or at 1 to get the new count?

After I put the spiders behind my back I said, "If we know that there are 13 insects and that there are 5 spiders to be added, how many would there be altogether?"

Lindsey immediately raised her hand and answered 18. She explained that she thought of 13 insects in her head and counted on 5 more spiders in her head.

Then I called on Mike. He recounted the 13 insects very carefully, one by one (in contrast to his earlier somewhat careless, random counting), and then touched and counted 5 imaginary spiders with one hand while raising 5 fingers, one at a time, on his other hand. Like Lindsey, he also came up with 18.

Liliana took a different approach. She counted the 13 insects and then separated 5 from that group and counted them on from the 13, also ending up with 18.

I brought the 5 spiders into view and together we all counted the 13 insects and 5 spiders to confirm that there really were 18.

These three students seem to represent a developmental sequence that children may go through in becoming comfortable with adding quantities together. Liliana started from 1, counted the 13 visible insects, and then separated 5 from that group as a concrete way to keep track of the additional 5 that she was counting. Mike seemed to be less dependent on the concrete objects. He also started at 1 with the 13 insects but then counted the additional 5 by touching imaginary spiders with one hand while keeping track with 5 fingers on his other hand. He seemed to have internalized that there are a total of 5 fingers on one of his hands, since he did not count out the 5 fingers before he counted them on. It did not seem to be a problem for him that his fingers can be labeled "1, 2, 3, 4, 5" in one situation and "14, 15, 16, 17, 18" in another situation. Liliana and Mike either did not recognize or did not trust that the 13 previously counted insects would still be 13, or they could not comfortably start counting in the middle of the number sequence. Lindsey, on the other hand, clearly

trusted that the new number included the original 13 and didn't feel a
need to start counting from 1. She seemed able to visualize a group that
she could label 13, plus 5 more individual spiders that she could easily
count on in her head. ⎸70

I wondered if the children had a sense of the commutative property
of addition, and decided to investigate. Would they recognize that we
would get the same answer whether we began with the 5 and added on
13, or began with 13 and added on 5?

I put the 13 insects behind my back, showed the children the 5 spiders, ⎸75
and asked how many there would be altogether if I were to add in
the missing 13. Many of the children immediately said 18. I raised the
question, "How do you know it is the same answer?" Although I can't
recall a clear answer from anyone, they gave variations on knowing that
there were still 13 insects and we had already counted 5 spiders. I asked ⎸80
if there was any way that we could count them all up by first using the
5 spiders that we could see. No one responded.

Were these children really understanding the commutative property
for addition? Or was the answer easy for them because there were no
new variables—that is, there were still *13 insects* and *5 spiders*? Even ⎸85
though I had changed the placement of each, the children may not have
seen this as a different situation. Would they have said so quickly that the
answer was still 18 if I had changed or eliminated a defining variable, for
example, if the 13 and the 5 were all insects?

I tried a problem with different numbers to see how they would deal ⎸90
with adding on a missing number of items that was more than 10: "What
if I told you there were 11 insects to add to the 5 spiders we already have
in front of us?" Liliana counted the 5 spiders that she saw. Then, without
counting out ten fingers beforehand, she continued counting on her
fingers one at a time to 15, and said she needed 1 more to make 16. ⎸95

I found it interesting that Liliana was not daunted by the fact that she
had only ten fingers. She seemed to have internalized that all her fingers
always make a group called "10" and 1 more finger makes another group
called "11." In addition, Liliana seemed comfortable with the fact that her
ten fingers could be called "1, 2, 3, 4, 5, 6, 7, 8, 9, 10" in one situation and ⎸100
"6, 7, 8, 9, 10, 11, 12, 13, 14, 15" in another.

To verify that the children understood the importance of one-to-one
correspondence in counting, I added 11 insects to the group of 5 spiders. I
counted the 5 carefully, and then I continued to count the extra 11 insects
randomly until I was way into the 20s. Many of the children shouted ⎸105
"No!" and said I could only count each insect once. Renaldo recounted

for the group, carefully moving and placing each one into a new group of already-counted insects. He got 16, confirming Liliana's answer.

Many of the children seem to understand the need for one-to-one correspondence and for only counting each item one time so that you get a specific answer that is repeatable. Many may have some sense of the commutative property for addition, but I cannot be sure of this without further investigation. Some of them clearly understand that a group of items has a constant value even when another group is added to them, and that it is not necessary to start over from 1 when adding the new items on one by one; others do not have this awareness or trust yet. Some interesting questions come up: When do children move from merely counting to actually understanding *addition*? Is it when they can count on from a number, rather than having to start again from 1? Or can children who have to start at 1 every time still understand that they are adding and not just counting?

C A S E   2

Going up and down with numbers

Wendy

KINDERGARTEN, MARCH

As we start each day in kindergarten, we assemble at the rug area for our opening meeting. One of the things we discuss is the number of children in school. This morning, as usual, we counted the number of boys, which today totaled 9, and then the number of girls, which totaled 8. I wrote on the chalkboard:

9 boys

8 girls

I then asked, "How many boys are out today?"

Natalie raised her hand and answered, "When all the boys are here, we have 10 boys, so today we have 9 boys, so 1 boy is out."

"How many girls are out today?"

Peter raised his hand and said, "It's 2." He knew that there were 10 girls in the class when all were present.

I asked, "How did you figure it out?"

Peter replied, "8 and 1 and . . . " He seemed to be stuck in his thinking. I feel he did figure it out correctly but then had trouble explaining.

I then asked, "Can someone else tell me how many girls are out today?"

Denisha's hand went up. She said, "It's 2, because 8 is 2 numbers down from 10."

"What does that mean?" I asked Denisha.

"When all the girls are here, it's 10," she told us. "You go down from 10 by 1, that's 9, and down 1 more, that's 8, so that's 2."

We usually count around the circle to find the total number in class for the day. I decided instead to see if the children could come up with the total just by looking at the numbers.

9 boys

8 girls

"How many kids here today?" I asked.

Daniel answered, "17."

I said, "Daniel, if you look at the numbers of boys and girls, can you tell me how you got 17?" He didn't reply. I think that Daniel counted around the circle and didn't want to tell me that.

Rachelle offered, "8 and 9 makes a 1 and a 7." When I asked Rachelle how she knew that, she answered, "I counted in my mind."

"How did you count in your mind? Say it out loud."

She began, "1, 2, 3, 4, 5, 6, 7, 8, 9 . . . " But she didn't go on. She wasn't using her fingers, so I'm not sure how she was going to explain the answer.

"Did anyone else figure it out in a different way?" I wondered.

Tamara's hand went up and she said, "It's 17, 8 and 9. Take 1 away from the 9, that makes it an 8, and 8 and 8 makes 16. So you put the 9 back. You go up one more from 8, you make a 9 and you have the 8, you get 17. You're going one more higher than 16."

I was amazed at how several of the children could see the relationship that numbers have to each other. They used the phrase "going up or down" to describe this. Tamara "went down" one from the 9 to make 8. It seemed easier for her to add 8 and 8, yet she knew that 9 was 1 more than 8 so the 16 had to "go up" by one. I feel that Peter was thinking about "going up" when he said 8 and 1, but couldn't say the 1 more to make 10. Denisha described "going down" from 10 by 1, and by 1 again to get 8. She then knew 2 girls were absent. Being able to go up and down with numbers seems to be a key to understanding number differences.

170

C A S E **3**

Complexities of counting back

Denise

GRADE 2, OCTOBER

I've been interested for the past year in the ways second graders come to understand addition, subtraction, and regrouping. I've watched children invent methods that reflect a tremendous amount of what I termed "sophistication" and flexibility in how they think about numbers. Among the "least sophisticated" methods for subtracting that I identified were kids counting backwards on their fingers, or collecting an amount of counters, say 22, for example, and then taking away 5.

175

180

I am also interested in seeing how kids move toward increasingly sophisticated and flexible thinking about number. In the first couple of weeks of school, I actively watched for examples that would help me begin to illuminate something (who knows just what?) about number sense. What I found was a surprise. I'm very interested in hearing if anyone is similarly puzzled, grabbed, or surprised by this event!

185

The activity we were working on is called "Enough for the Class" (from *Counting, Coins, and Combinations*, in the curriculum *Investigations in Number, Data, and Space*, 2nd ed., Pearson Learning, 2008). I show my class a bag of cubes and tell them we need to figure out if there are enough cubes in the bag for everyone in our class to take one. If there are too many or too few, *how many* too many or too few are there?

190

As a class we counted the cubes in the bag and found that there were 32. We had 25 students in our class that day.

195

Denise

I witnessed students solving this problem in a variety of ways. Some solved it by adding on their fingers from 25 to 32 and getting 7. Others solved it by counting backwards from 32 until they got to 25. Others saw that by adding 5 to 25 they got to 30 quickly, and then added 2 more to the 5. Some solved it with cubes stacked to a length of 32, taking off cubes until there were 25.

Susan counted backwards and recorded her method on her paper like this: 32 | | | | | | | 25. She got 6 for her answer.

The next day when we discussed different students' methods, there was general agreement that 7 was the answer. I called on Susan, hoping she'd talk about her method. Instead, she used a strip of 32 cubes that a classmate had just used. She took off 7 cubes one by one and indeed got 25. (I was a little disappointed; I had hoped she would bring her method to the class.) Then her face looked puzzled and she said, "But I remember yesterday I got 6."

I said, "But today you got 7. Hmm. How could that be?"

Susan repeated her process with 32 cubes, recounting to be sure there were really 32 cubes in her strip and then carefully taking off 7 and recounting those remaining 25 cubes again. She was very puzzled.

Other students restated their process that gave them the answer 7, and Susan was still puzzled. I asked her to look again at her paper and reminded her, "Didn't you count backwards, Susan?"

Susan looked at her work from the previous day more closely. "Oh yes, I did."

I drew on the board what Susan had drawn yesterday, 32 | | | | | | | 25, and said, "This is what Susan drew. There's the 6."

Some children said, "Yeah, there's 6."

This was a genuine confusion for a few minutes as students buzzed about how they had got 7, but here was Susan getting 6 one way and 7 another.

In a few seconds Clara said, "Well, Susan has to take away either the 32 or the 25 in order to get 7."

I said, "Right, but why?"

Several other children offered up how and why 7 was in fact the answer. They pointed out that with 32 cubes, you are taking away the 32nd cube, the 31st cube, the 30th cube, the 29th, the 28th, the 27th, and the 26th cube, and then you are left with 25 cubes.

Denise

GRADE 2, OCTOBER

	7 6 5 4 3 2 1
25 cubes	26 27 28 29 30 31 32

But when you count backwards on your fingers or out loud, you start at 32 and don't count 1 until you get to 31, then 2 is at 30, 3 is at 29, 4 is at 28, 5 is at 27, 6 is at 26, and when you count back the 7th time, you get to 25.

235

There are 25 left!

$32 - \boxed{6} = 25$

$32 - \boxed{7} = 25$

Drawing these diagrams myself much later highlighted the complexities in a method I had always assumed was "less sophisticated." Indeed, this counting backwards does seem simple at first glance. But, if I didn't know already that 32 take away 7 is 25, how would I construct and make sense of the difference between these two ways of thinking? In my quest to investigate number sense and to identify how children develop it, this moment really sits with me still.

240

In fact, this issue came up several weeks later when we were considering how many kids are here in class if 4 of them are absent. Ricky reasoned similarly to Susan's first assertion in my earlier example, that 26 . . . 25 (1) . . . 24 (2) . . . 23 (3) . . . 22 (4), and there's 21 left. So there must be 21 kids here.

245

Many children spoke up quickly and heatedly, insisting that they knew 22 plus 4 is 26, so if there are 4 kids *not* here, there must be 22 here. Others clamored that Ricky had to take away the 26 first, or that he got to 22 as he took away the 4th kid. Many of my students are quite convinced and clear about how they would take 4 away from 26. Ricky and Susan have simply piqued my interest about how they will *become* convinced, now that I consider some of the complexities of what might or might not happen in their construct.

250

255

Making Meaning for Operations

C A S E   4

Missing part versus missing change

Kina

GRADE 1, JANUARY

I went over to work with Zenobia on a story problem because she looked horribly confused. This was the problem:

> Max had 3 blocks. He found some more blocks. Then he had
> 7 blocks. How many blocks did he find? 260

Zenobia had 3 cubes and 7 cubes and wasn't sure what to do. She counted all of them and got 10, but she looked at me with confusion and said, "I know that's not the answer."

We acted out the problem (or rather, I acted it out). I said, "Max had 3 blocks. Here are the 3 blocks. Then he found some. Oh, look, here are 265 some more blocks. Now he has 7 blocks. So he had 3, got some more, and both of those together made 7, right?"

Zenobia looked at me, and I could tell that she was trying to understand it, but it was just too much. So I said, "If you're still not sure you understand, it is OK to say, 'I'm still confused.'" 270

She said, "I'm still confused."

Then I wondered if making a connection to something more familiar would help her, so I brought her back to another activity, one at which she is routinely successful. I said, "Let's put this aside for a moment and solve another problem. Pretend that you and I are playing 'How Many 275 Am I Hiding?' We're playing with 6 cubes. I have some behind my back. You can see 2. You know that there are 6 cubes all together. How many am I hiding?"

Zenobia thought and said, "Four."

I asked, "Does it remind you of anything we've just been doing?" 280

Zenobia replied, "Not really."

I said, "OK, then let's pretend that Max was playing 'How Many Am I Hiding?' He could see 3. Some were behind his friend's back. He knew the total was 7. How many were hiding?"

Zenobia thought and then said, "Four." 285

I asked, "OK, so do you see any connections between this problem and the other Max problem?"

She said, "Yes, there's a 3 and a 7. I just don't get it, still."

After that, Zenobia and I took a break from the problem. Sometimes you spend so much time on something that it just becomes too much. So 290 she went to work on some other math problems.

For me, the connection between the story problem and the "How Many Am I Hiding?" game seems so obvious. What is the connection Zenobia needs to make? And what about her classmates? I am thinking about how to start a class discussion to see what ideas students might 295 have about the connections between the game and the story problems.

C A S E 5

Valentine stickers

Jody
GRADES 1 AND 2, JANUARY

When the children arrive each morning, right away they start work on the problem of the day, which I have written on a chart or on the chalk-board. One day last week, I had this word problem displayed:

> **?** Sabrina and Yvonne have 14 stickers when they put their 300
> stickers together. Yvonne has 6 stickers. How many stickers
> does Sabrina have?

Solving the problem of the day has become a routine in my class; after settling in, the children just go and get any materials they need (cubes, links, counters) to solve the problem. They know that they have to keep a 305 record of their strategies for solving the problem, using models, pictures, words, or number sentences, so that they would be able to explain their thinking process to someone else.

This is how Latasha, a first grader, solved the problem. First she drew 14 hearts on her paper (see next page). Then she wrote numbers 1 to 6 310 inside the first 6 hearts. Then she started again, writing from 1 to 8 on the remaining hearts. She marked off the first 6 hearts. Below her picture of hearts, she wrote 6 + 8 = 14.

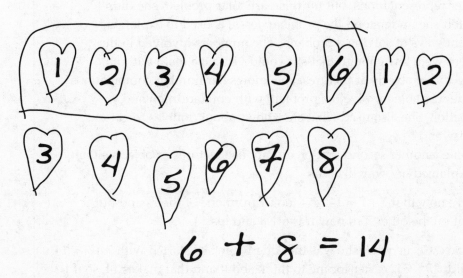

Most adults would think of this as a subtraction problem, but Latasha represented it with an addition sentence. When I saw what she was doing, I wanted to make sure that she was clear about her process and that she understood the problem. I asked Latasha what the 14 was. She said that this was the number of stickers Sabrina and Yvonne had together. When I asked her how many stickers Sabrina had, she quickly pointed to the hearts labeled 1 to 8 that she had not put a circle around and said, "Sabrina has 8 stickers." Her responses assured me that she understood what the problem was and that her strategy was clear to her.

Jessie, a second grader, did not draw a picture for this problem. Instead she wrote the following on her paper:

If Yvonne has 6 stickers and they have 14 altogether, I figured it out by minusing 6 from 14.

14 − 6 = 8

I also figured it out like this:

6 + ____ = 14

I know that 6 + 6 = 12, add 2 more = 14, so

6 + 8 = 14

Having known Jessie for over a year now, since she was in my
first-grade class last year, I know that she feels comfortable explaining
her thinking process using numbers. Sometimes she uses pictures
or other representations, but for this particular problem she didn't,   335
and I felt she understood the problem. Jessie is used to explaining
different ways of solving a problem. The numbers involved in the
problem were low enough that she could visualize them without
having to use objects or pictures. She knows her number combinations
and she was able to solve the problem with both addition and   340
subtraction. She also used what she knows about doubles to get
her answer.

Cecile, another second grader, did not use pictures or objects either.
She explained her way like this:

> I know that 7 + 7 = 14, so I took 1 from one of the 7s and put   345
> it on the other 7 so now it is 6 + 8 and it's 14.

I asked Cecile what she was thinking when she started with 7 + 7 = 14.
She said, "7 + 7 is easier for me to think about and that makes 14, so if I
move 1 from one of the 7s to the other, I have 6 + 8 and that is 14."
Cecile feels comfortable with renaming addends that add up to the   350
same number. One of our daily routines is thinking of many different
ways to rename a number using doubles, addition, and subtraction.
Cecile often thinks of numbers that are easier and more convenient for
her to deal with, to help her solve problems.

Maya is a first grader. For the sticker problem, she took 14 cubes and   355
made a tower. Then she took 6 cubes and made another tower. She lined
up the two towers next to each other, like this:

When she counted how many cubes there were beyond her 6-cube
tower, she found that there were 8.

When I saw what Maya had done, I was struck by the fact that   360
her model consisted of more than 14 cubes. I asked her what the 8
cubes represented, and she said it was Sabrina's stickers. She said that
the 6-cube tower below the 14-cube tower was only a way for her to

remember how many stickers Yvonne had. She was using the extra 6
cubes as a marker so that she could easily see how many stickers Sabrina
had. I then asked her what the 14 cubes represented, and she said that
these were the stickers that Yvonne and Sabrina had together. Maya could
explain her process clearly by using objects, but when I asked her if she
could tell me a math sentence that showed what she had just done, she
was not able to do it.

Joachim, a second grader, had drawn this on his paper:

Joachim's model confused me at first, so I asked him to explain his
process. This is what he said:

> I took two 6s and added them. That is 12. But this is not the
> correct number so I added 2 to the 12 and it is 14. So now it is
> $6 + 6 + 2 = 14$. And $6 + 8 = 14$.

Joachim's way is similar to Cecile's. They both relied on their
knowledge of doubles to get to the right number.

I asked Damien, who had chosen to use a number strip, how he solved
the problem. He put his finger on 6 and said, "I started counting up from
6 until I got to 14, and I counted 8." As I listened to him count, he said
"1" as he pointed to 7, "2" as he pointed to 8, and kept moving up until

he said "8" as he pointed to 14. Damien also made 14 circles on his paper
and counted off 6 by putting a line across each of 6 circles. There were 8
circles left.

385

6   8

Antoinette used cubes to help her solve the problem. She explained
her process like this:

> Since Yvonne has 6 stickers, I took 6 cubes. Then I said,
> how many more cubes should I take to get to 14, and then I
> counted up until I got to 14, and there were 8 more.

390

When I asked Antoinette to show me how she counted up from 6,
she said, "6 . . . [*pause*], 7, 8, 9, 10, 11, 12, 13, 14." Her way of solving the
problem is similar to Damien's first way. Although they had different
materials, both used counting up to solve the problem.

Kim, a second grader, and Dylan, a first grader, were working together
and role-playing the problem, pretending that one of them was Yvonne
and the other was Sabrina. They counted 14 teddy bear counters together.
Then Kim said, "I am Yvonne and you are Sabrina. I have 6 teddy bears.
How many teddy bears do you have?" Dylan, acting as Sabrina, counted
his teddy bears and he exclaimed, "I have 8. So Sabrina has 8 stickers!"
They were having a good time pretending, and when I left them, I asked
them to try to think of another way to solve the same problem.

395

400

All the children had appropriate solution methods. They used
methods that were familiar to them; some used number combinations
that were easy for them to think about. They understood the problem
and were able to explain their strategies and represent the problem in
different ways. My goal for all my students is that they feel comfortable
in communicating their thinking process while also expanding their
repertoire of strategies for problem solving. I encourage them to try
solving a problem in more than one way and to share their strategies with
someone else. I also would like my students to explore the properties of
addition and subtraction. Jessie, who used the operations, knew that the
problem could be solved by either addition or subtraction.

405

410

CASE 6

Finding the difference:
Should I add or subtract?

Machiko

GRADE 4, NOVEMBER

My students had been exploring the relationship between addition and subtraction for several weeks. They had worked with related problems such as $125 + 34 =$ _____ and $159 -$ ___ $= 34$. We had also been exploring the meaning of the equals sign with problems such as $74 + 22 = 80 +$ ____. I was interested in finding out how they might apply the ideas and strategies they were developing to a problem that asked them to consider the difference between two numbers.

What does "difference" mean?

I offered the class this problem to think about:
    Find two numbers whose difference is 153.
    After a few minutes of watching their individual work, I realized I needed to bring the class together to talk about what it meant to find the difference between two numbers. I said, "As I walked around, I noticed that you were approaching the problem in many ways. I am wondering what you all are thinking about. What do you think it means to find the difference?"

CHLOE: It is what you get when you add.

TREY: I think that is the sum.

ALEX: It is when you subtract.

KATIE: On the number line, it is how far apart two numbers are; I think they meant to write the distance.

415

420

425

430

Machiko

I asked Katie if she could show us what she meant. She came up to 435
number line we have posted on our wall and pointed to 10 and then 20,
saying, "These are 10 away from each other." Then Tara chimed in.

TARA: 20 is 10 away from 30.

TEACHER: We can say that 20 is 10 away from 30, and we can also say
             that the *difference* between 20 and 30 is 10.   440

JOE: [*coming up to the number line and pointing at 30*] And the
             difference between 30 and 40 is 10!

KATIE: I just put 0 in the calculator and then added 153, and I got
             153. If I put in a number and add 153 to it, I get a number
             that would be 153 more.   445

TEACHER: How could we use Katie's idea to find more numbers that
              have a difference of 153?

KATIE: I can make a pattern now. [*She comes to the board and writes.*]

             1 + 153 = 154

             2 + 153 = 155   450

I was unsure whether the class was relating the addend to which 153
was being added and the resulting sum as having a difference of 153. I
wondered if using an unmarked number line might highlight the idea
of the *difference* between two numbers. How would the students connect
Katie's addition equations to the placement of the numbers and the   455
distance between those numbers on a number line? Would they recognize
a similar subtraction problem that could be modeled by the same
numbers on a number line?

Since a few students had already used our posted number line to talk
about differences of 10, I said, "A few minutes ago, Joe and Katie came 460
up and showed us numbers that were 10 apart, or had a difference of 10,
on the number line. I wonder what the numbers Katie has written on the
board would look like on a number line."

22   Making Meaning for Operations

Reesa enthusiastically volunteered to come up and show her thinking. She drew a number line: | 465

REESA: You start at 1, and then you hop 153 to land on 154.

TEACHER: So, how does what Reesa drew on the board help us find two numbers whose difference is 153?

LEANA: See, the 1 plus the hop of 153 is 154.

JOE: Ohh… the 1 is 153 different than the 154. | 470

ALEX: We can put the 2 on the row.

TEACHER: What are you thinking about, Alex?

ALEX: Put the 2 on the line, and also put the 153.

TREY: But the 153 is the jump. We need to put 155.

TESSA: And then put a 3 and a 156! | 475

Lots of voices started offering comments, and many thumbs were up requesting air time. I asked the class to talk in their small groups about what they were noticing and thinking. As I walked around, students were continuing Katie's pattern in their math journals and talking about how they would place the numbers on the number line. Were they noticing | 480 that each time they came up with two new numbers, those numbers were the same distance apart on the number line?

The number line seemed to allow the students to form a visual image for the pattern Katie had offered. They were now exploring a method for finding many pairs of numbers with a difference of 153. | 485 After a few minutes, we came back together to discuss what ideas were developing.

TEACHER: What are some ideas or questions your group talked about?

TREY: Why are we adding 153? I thought we should subtract it.

There was no response to his question! A few seconds of silence and confused looks followed. I was glad for the wait time as I was thinking about where his question might now lead the discussion.

CHLOE: [*pointing to Katie's addition sentences*] Yeah, this isn't subtraction.

BRAD: When we're jumping on the number line, we're adding 153.

LEANA: I took a number and took away 153. That is subtracting.

TREY: But Katie added.

EMILY: I think it works both ways. We can add or subtract.

JOE: Add or subtract what?

TEACHER: How about if we pick a number and try out your ideas?

ALEX: Let's use 77.

Emily came up to the board and drew a new number line.

I was interested that she had placed 77 in the middle of the line. But before I could ask her about her representation, Donny spoke up, saying "Add 153, like Katie did."

Donny came up and made a jump of 153, landing on 230.

The class decided to check 77 + 153 on the calculator.

EMILY: So 77 is 153 away from 230, but why did he add?

ALEX: Because the difference means one is more than the other, and the 230 is 153 more.

TEACHER: 230 is 153 more than what?

BRAD: Than 77. So if we add 153 to a number, we get one number that is 153 more than the other number.

TOSHANA: Yes, you can see it here [*pointing to the jump of 153 on the line*].

LEANA: Remember, I subtracted.   515

TEACHER: Leana, show us how you subtracted.

Leana came to the number line and, starting at 230, showed a jump backward of 153 to land on 77.

ALEX: You can subtract or add 153. Those two are basically the same. $1 + 153 = 154$ and $154 - 153 = 1$.   520

Throughout the small- and whole-group discussions, the students had been moving back and forth between addition and subtraction as they thought about the difference between two numbers. I was intrigued by the way the numbers they chose affected their thinking about the relationship between the operations of addition and subtraction.   525

TEACHER: How many numbers do you think have a difference of 153?

TESSA: A lot of numbers, because you can add lots of numbers to get 153. Like $150 + 3$, or $151 + 2$.

ALEX: But those don't have a difference of 153; they equal 153.

TESSA: Oh, those are combinations that equal 153.   530

ALEX: I think there are all the numbers that you can add to 153. They will never end.

TEACHER: Let's think about Tessa's idea of adding numbers that equal 153. Are there any numbers that we can add, and those numbers will still have a difference of 153?   535

KATIE: Only zero!

DONNY: Because $0 + 153$ equals 153, and you would have to hop 153 from 0 to get to 153.

Machiko

Subtracting a greater number from a lesser number

Alex took us back to the number line on which Donny had showed
77 + 153 = 230.

540

ALEX: We can also subtract 153 from 77.

TEACHER: Can we show that on the number line we have up here?

DONNY: No, because it will go past the 0. Then it won't be 153 away.

ALEX: Yes, we can, but it will be negative.

545

TEACHER: So, do you all want to try and subtract to see what happens?

BRAD: Yes, let's jump the other way!

EMILY: I think we will land on negative 230, because now we are
subtracting.

Brad came up and made a jump of 153 to the left of the 77.

550

JOE: What are we going to put there?

TOSHANA: I subtracted 153 – 77 on the calculator and I got 76.

TESSA: I subtracted 77 – 153 and I got a minus 76.

ALEX: You can subtract 153 from a bigger number. Like 179. But not
from smaller numbers.

555

EMILY: You can use smaller numbers than 153, but you will go into
the negative.

BRAD: And you can subtract or add.

CHLOE: We can write 77 + 153 or 77 – 153?

REESA: You can do either one.

560

ALEX: I can show the other hop on the number line. We already
figured out that 77 – 153 is minus 76 on the calculator.

Machiko

Alex then came up and made a hop to 0 and then a hop to –76. It was interesting that he had made the stop at 0 before he hopped to –76. I wondered if the class was thinking about what the distances of the two smaller hops were.

TEACHER: What is the difference between 77 and 0?

I heard many voices call out 77. Donny asked if he could put a 77 on the hop. After he recorded that on the board, I continued by asking, "What about the small hop that is left?"

TESSA: 77.

CHLOE: 76.

DONNY: It has to be 76, because 76 + 77 is 153.

ALEX: The two hops have to be the same as the big hop of 153.

Assessing what students learned

A few days later, I offered students a new problem:

> Find two numbers whose difference is 58.

> Find two numbers whose difference is 134.

Much of their work indicated that the unmarked number line was an integral part of their strategies. Figures 1.1 to 1.5 are representative of the work of the class.

Figure 1.1   Donny uses 134 as a starting number to find numbers that have a difference of 134

Figure 1.2   Reesa finds pairs of numbers that have a difference of 58

Figure 1.3   Brad represents two numbers that have a difference of 134 from 100

Machiko

Figure 1.4 Katie represents two numbers that have a difference of 134

0 and 134
1 and 135
2 and 136
3 and 137
4 and 138
5 and 139
6 and 140
7 and 141
8 and 142
9 and 143
10 and 144
11 and 145
12 and 146
13 and 147

134

Patterns

When you add
one to one
number, you
have to add
one to the
other number
to keep the same
defference

Figure 1.5 Alex uses a pattern to find many pairs of numbers with a difference of 134

I was left reflecting on the students' variety of strategies for thinking about the difference between two numbers. How do students develop a multifaceted meaning for a word like *difference*? How was the relationship between addition and subtraction highlighted for students as they explored how to find two numbers that have a specified difference? Would they have observed that the difference could be either an addend or a subtrahend without the models of the number lines?

585

Chapter 1

CASE 7

Number line models for subtraction

Carl

GRADE 7, JUNE

We are coming to the end of another school year and I am thinking about the importance of models for student learning in mathematics. Students in my classes have used balance models for equations; rectangle and groups-of-groups models for the distributive property; number-line, chip, and savings-debt models for operations with negative numbers; and tables, graphs, equations, and walking-rate models for understanding linear relationships. Models help students make sense of mathematical ideas in a way that connects to their own understandings. Without models, students are dependent on the teacher- or text-provided algorithms, which may or may not make sense to them. With models, students can use the contextual clues of the materials or situation to help them sort out and justify effective versus invalid strategies and ideas.

I decided to take students back to a basic operation to see how they would now use a model to make sense of that operation. I assigned two problems, asking students to use a number line to show how they thought about and solved them.

1. I have $465. I spend $180 on video games. How much money do I have left for my trip to Hawaii?

2. I am taking a trip to visit a friend in another state. I drive 180 miles and then stop to rest. The total distance to my friend's house is 465 miles. How much farther do I have to go?

The take-away strategy was by far the most prevalent approach for problem 1. With this strategy, students would start at 465 on the number line and then go back (left) 180 units toward 0. They used a variety of methods to do this. Howard showed an arching line from 465 to 365, then another arching line from 365 to 300, and finally an arching line from 300 to 285. I asked him to explain this and he said, "465 minus 100 is 365, and 365 minus 65 is 300. I have used up 165 of 180, so I need 15 more to use up all 180."

Tina showed arching lines of 20 each to get from 465 back to 285.

Figure 1.6 Two number-line approaches to problem 1

The adding-up or difference-between strategy was by far the most prevalent approach for problem 2. Mark put a big dot at 180 and at 465. He then showed arching lines from 180 to 200, 200 to 400, and 400 to 465. Above these lines he wrote the number 285. Denali's diagram looked similar, but he had arching lines that went 10 at a time from 180 to 460.

Figure 1.7 Two number-line approaches to problem 2

I asked the class why most of them had used take-away for the first problem and some other method for the second problem.

Alexis explained, "In the first problem, you have some money and you are giving it to the cashier. With the second problem, you want to know how far it is from one place to another. They just feel different."

Ian added, "It is like looking a map. With the second problem, you are looking at a map that shows where you are and where you are going. You want to know how far that is."

The explanations of Alexis and Ian highlight how a model can influence the action a student sees in a problem. Different strategies can

Carl

feel like a better match for one kind of action than another. In the first problem, the context conveys an action of taking away. I have some money and then money is taken away. The number line approach of starting at 465 and working back feels more consistent. In the second problem, the context conveys the idea of finding the distance between. Putting marks at 180 and 465 and finding what lies between feels more like how people use a map, which is what students would use for a car trip.

I am now wondering what this difference in strategies means to these seventh graders. Do they see these as the same operation, or do they view them as different operations? How do they make sense of take-away strategies and adding-up strategies representing the same problem of 465 − 180? If I asked them to write a number sentence for both of these problems, would they write 465 − 180 = 285 for both, or would they write 180 + n = 465 for the second?

All year long we have been using fact families to help us with operations involving decimals, fractions, and negative numbers. Do they see the connection of these two problems to fact families? I also wonder what kind of instructional moves would help students to make and leverage these connections. I can see them, but do they? What kinds of classroom discussion move this beyond simply solving two different problems to deepening their understanding of subtraction?

Although the two strategies described were the most common, students also used strategies that took advantage of other ideas we had worked with during the year. Negative number strategies came up in a couple of different ways. For problem 1, Akeem started his number line at negative 180 and then showed an arching line going up 465 to positive 285. At first, I thought he had completely abandoned the context of the problem and created a problem that he knew gave the same answer. When I asked him how his model fit the context, he said, "My dad usually pays for the stuff with his credit card and I pay him back. I would owe him $180, but I have $465. So after I pay off the $180 that I owe, I have $285 left over."

465

−180   0   285

Carl

GRADE 7, JUNE

Terra started her number line at negative 465 and drew an arching line that went 180 to the right, to negative 285. When I asked her to explain how this matched the context, she could not. She did not seem to be concerned that her answer ended up being negative 285 instead of positive 285.

670

After a couple of students shared their negative number strategies, a number of other methods surfaced. Ivan said that he subtracted a negative 180 to get the answer. Other students disagreed with his method, but they had to use other models (such as the chip model) to convince everyone that Ivan's method would give an answer of 465 + 180, not 465 – 180. The original context was not useful in making sense of this method or Ivan's confusion.

675

CHAPTER 2

Making meaning for multiplication and division

CASE 8	Bunnies and eggs	*Bella, Kindergarten, April*
CASE 9	Early multiplication	*Nisha, Grade 2, March*
CASE 10	Candy canes in packages	*Janine, Grade 4, December*
CASE 11	How do kids think about division?	*Georgia, Grades 3 and 4, October*
CASE 12	Are these kids or seeds?	*Melinda, Grade 2, November*

As we move from addition and subtraction to multiplication and division, the questions that were posed in chapter 1 still apply, and we extend them to all four operations:

- When we see different number sentences that can model a single situation, what do we learn about relationships among operations?

- What does it mean to have a *concept* of addition, subtraction, multiplication, or division?

- What can we see about the operations through different representations (cubes, number lines)?

Furthermore, multiplication and division come with their own questions:

- What kinds of situations are modeled by multiplication and division?

- What issues must students work through in order to make sense of these operations?

- What ideas about addition and subtraction do students bring to their work with multiplication and division?

Ponder and take notes on these questions as you read through the following cases from kindergarten through grade 4. After reading the cases, review the questions again.

C A S E **8**

Bunnies and eggs

Bella

Kindergarten, April

Since Easter was coming up, I decided to do some problems about bunny rabbits. After a discussion on the number of legs one bunny rabbit has, I drew a picture of a bunny on the chalkboard and asked the children to solve the following problem:

 If one bunny has 4 legs, how many legs would 3 bunnies have?

5

I told them that they could use any manipulative they wished to solve the problem. I was quite interested in the various representations they came up with.

Jason built his rabbits from colored wooden blocks; each rabbit had a head, a body, and four legs. He came over to me and said, "Mrs. Waters, I got 12 legs." I asked him how he got the answer, and he told me he counted them. I asked him to draw me a picture of what he had done. Figure 2.1 shows his drawing.

10

Bella

Rashad used the large plastic keys we keep in a bucket in the room. He placed one key horizontally for each body, four keys perpendicular to it for the legs, and made three of these arrangements (see Figure 2.2).

I asked, "How many legs did you get?" and Rashad told me 12. When I asked him to show me how he got 12, he counted, pointing to each "leg" in turn. I was surprised that he didn't get confused about which keys were legs and which represented the body.

Carlita also used keys to represent the problem. First she made one row of four keys and told me that she had one rabbit. I asked her where the other rabbits were, and she said she would make them. I watched her build a second row of four keys, and then a third row (see Figure 2.3).

"See, I have 3 rabbits."

"How many legs are there in all?" I asked.

Carlita counted her keys: "Twelve."

Figure 2.1 Jason's drawing of three bunnies, four legs each

Figure 2.2 Rashad's arrangement of keys, another way of representing three bunnies

Figure 2.3 Carlita's arrangement of keys, showing four legs for each of three rabbits

Bella

KINDERGARTEN, APRIL

Figure 2.4 Kenya's picture of cubes representing three four-legged bunnies

Kenya used Unifix cubes, snapping together three groups of orange and white cubes in an a-b-a-b pattern. She counted them all together to get her answer and made a picture of what she had done (see Figure 2.4).

When I got to Flora, she had a row of 12 rocks in front of her (see Figure 2.5).

"How many legs did you get?"

"I got 12."

"Can you tell me how you did it?"

"I counted one bunny first; then I counted the next bunny's; then I counted the next bunny."

"So how did you know how many legs there were in all?"

"I counted all of them."

Mark, Quincy, and Jerome were busy building their rabbits out of Legos®. They built great looking rabbits with four legs, but time ran out before they could solve the problem.

The children were all so engaged in solving the problem that, even when I announced lunch time, they didn't want to leave. There was no one in the group who was not working on the problem.

Figure 2.5 Flora's rocks, representing the 12 legs on three bunnies

Bella

The children enjoyed being given the problem to solve, though I was aware that some of them still have difficulty counting even those small numbers. Besides the children whose representations I have described here, there were some who were not able to figure out the total. 50

Several days later, I decided to give a similar problem; this time I wanted to see what was going on with the children who had difficulty. 55

? I made 3 Easter baskets for my friends. In each basket, I put 3 eggs. How many eggs were there in all?

Again, I told the children they could use whatever manipulatives they might choose.

Jenna used the Unifix cubes. First she made a unit of 3 cubes and brought them over to show me. I asked her what she had, and she said that she had one basket. 60

"Where are the other baskets?" I asked.

"I haven't made them yet," she said, heading back to the table. Soon she was back again, this time with two units of 3. 65

"How many baskets do you have now?"

"Two."

"How many baskets did I say were needed?"

"Three."

"Where are they?" 70

Jenna went off again and returned with the third unit of 3. "How many eggs do you have?" I asked.

"I don't know. I haven't counted them yet." She proceeded to count all the cubes and soon arrived at her answer: 9 eggs.

Jenna really surprised me with her understanding of the problem. She very rarely participates in an activity in a way that helps me understand what she really knows. Today I was impressed. 75

Junior also worked with Unifix cubes. He had 3 orange ones, 3 white, and 3 yellow.

"What do you have?" I asked. 80

"Three baskets."

"How many eggs are in each basket?"

"Three."

"How many eggs do you have in all?"

"Three." 85

Junior showed me how he counted: Each unit of 3 was "one" to him. I took one unit and broke it apart. He counted them, "1, 2, 3," and agreed that they represented 3 eggs. I put them back together with the other two units of 3 and asked him how many eggs were there. Again he said, "Three." I tried several ways to help him see that I wanted him to count the individual cubes, but it didn't help. He was unable to see the difference or sameness between cubes once they became a single unit of 3.

Several of the children had no difficulty with this problem, so for them I posed an extension:

> **?** If I added 1 more egg to each basket, how many eggs would there be?

When I gave the second problem to Mark and Quincy, they both went away and soon returned with an answer. Mark explained, "I put 3 more on the 3 baskets. One more egg to 3 baskets, and that makes 12." Quincy had the same answer, but when I asked him how he got it, he said, "Mark told me."

Jason presented me with three groups of 3 Unifix cubes to demonstrate his answer of 9 to the first problem. When I asked him to solve the second problem, he added only a single cube and said there were 10. I repeated the question at least twice to see if he could figure out what was wrong with his answer and how he could fix it, but he did not change his answer.

Rashad had no problem figuring out the first problem, using an arrangement of three rows of 3 keys each. When I gave him the second problem, he added 1 key to each group and said there were 12 eggs. Seeing how easily he arrived at the answer, I decided to challenge him with another extension:

> **?** I have another friend, and I would also like to give this friend an Easter basket with the same number of eggs. How many eggs would there be in all?

"I added one more basket," he said. "Four baskets with 4 eggs: 16." Only after he gave an answer did he count the added keys. "See, I was right!" Rashad, it seems, has an ability to think about numbers at a level beyond his age.

As usual, I was unable to get around to all the children, but I learned more about what my class knows and how they handle problems. A couple of years ago, I wouldn't have attempted *any* of this kind of mathematics with children of this age. I would have thought that this is too difficult for them. How wrong I would have been!

CASE 9

Early multiplication

Nisha

GRADE 2, MARCH

Recently, as I observed second-grade students working on a variety
of tasks, I wondered how they were seeing multiplication. Were they
using count-by strategies (such as counting by fives) or repeated
addition to find the total number of units in the various pieces? Were
they seeing area? | 125

To find out, I posed this task. I provided colored tiles and asked
students to build this figure, which I projected on the overhead. | 130

I then asked students to think about ways that they might determine
the total number of tiles in this figure, without counting the tiles one by
one.

I purposely chose a figure that allowed students to connect with
area models, but was different in that it was not a complete rectangle. I
wanted to see how and in what ways students might recognize and use
the rectangles embedded in this figure to simplify their process of finding
the total number of tiles. In other words, would they see the rectangles
and know their areas? | 135 | 140

After students had time to build the figure and think privately for a
couple of minutes, I pulled the group together to share some ideas before
they actually set out to find the total number of tiles. Christopher quickly
offered, "I see five groups of three." I asked him to come up to the
overhead and show where he was seeing those groups. | 145

As Christopher pointed to the groups he saw, I recorded his thinking
on an enlarged paper version of the figure by putting loops around

groups of 3, modeling how I wanted students to record their thinking by showing the groups they see and generating an expression.

3 + 3 + 3 + 3 + 3

When I asked for a number sentence that I could use to describe his method, Christopher told me that he would write 3 + 3 + 3 + 3 + 3 = ?. I recorded this on the recording sheet as well, but I was surprised that he had given me a repeated addition statement after telling me that there were five groups of 3. Was this related to the way in which I recorded his thinking with the loops, or had he been thinking repeated addition all along?

Then Patrick spoke up. He said "The figure is just 3 times 4 plus 3." I asked him if he was seeing the same groups that Christopher had shared or if he saw something else.

I really didn't intend to discuss more than one strategy before I set students off to work, but now Patrick's idea was out there. So I repeated what Patrick said and asked the class who had an idea about what Patrick might be seeing. I told the class that once they thought they saw something, they should give me a thumbs-up. Then I had Patrick come up to the overhead to share his thinking while I recorded on the enlarged paper version of the figure.

Patrick said, "I see this 3-by-4 rectangle [*pointing to the dimensions of the rectangle*], with the extra group of three right here [*looping this group with his fingers*]."

3 × 4 + 3

Nisha

I now asked students to work independently to come up with some
more ideas about how to see and count the total number of tiles in the
figure. I distributed a recording sheet that had three copies of the figure,
with space on the right of each figure to record number sentences.

I knew that some students already had three ideas in mind before I
distributed these sheets, as the opening discussion had taken longer than
I intended. I suggested that if they had more than three ways of thinking
about this, they could record additional methods on the back. For an
extra challenge, they might want to sketch a larger figure, like this one
but with more tiles, and show how they would see and count the total
number of tiles.

As I monitored their individual work, I commented on things I was
seeing that I wanted all the students to consider as they recorded their
counting methods: "I like the way that Ashley has recorded more than
one number sentence next to her method of counting the tiles. . . . I
appreciate how Karissa is using color to communicate her thinking."

I then noticed that Bethany was already working on the back of her
paper, sketching a very large figure. Below it she wrote $10 \times 11 + 10 = 120$.
I asked her how she figured that out, and she pointed up to the poster
on the wall that lists multiplication problems. I didn't think these were
facts she knew, but I was happy to see that she was using the available
resources and not just counting squares one by one.

I next asked students to share their strategies in groups of two or
three. I encouraged them to show their recordings so that others could
easily follow along. I explained that once everyone in the group had
shared, they were to choose their favorite counting method and record
it on an enlarged copy of the figure, to prepare for sharing their method
with the rest of the class.

As pairs or trios shared their visuals with the whole class, I recorded
the number sentences that they suggested for their counting strategy
The results, with their corresponding numbers statements, are shown in
Figure 2.6.

I was encouraged by the conversation sparked by these visual
displays. Students often commented, "I got that one." They also
contributed additional number statements for some of these. For example,
in response to Karissa and Bethany's strategy "$4 + 4 + 4 + 4 - 1$," Kristina
suggested that they could also "multiply 4 times 4, since there are
4 groups of 4."

Nisha

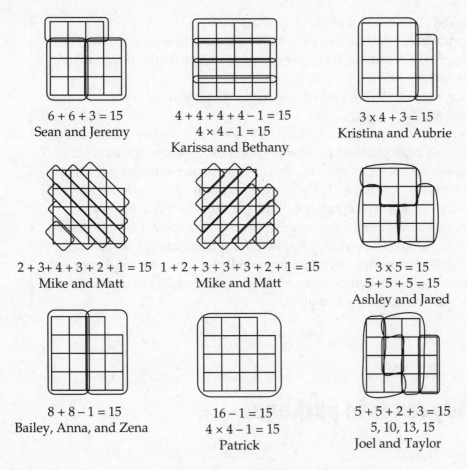

6 + 6 + 3 = 15
Sean and Jeremy

4 + 4 + 4 + 4 − 1 = 15
4 × 4 − 1 = 15
Karissa and Bethany

3 x 4 + 3 = 15
Kristina and Aubrie

2 + 3 + 4 + 3 + 2 + 1 = 15
Mike and Matt

1 + 2 + 3 + 3 + 3 + 2 + 1 = 15
Mike and Matt

3 x 5 = 15
5 + 5 + 5 = 15
Ashley and Jared

8 + 8 − 1 = 15
Bailey, Anna, and Zena

16 − 1 = 15
4 × 4 − 1 = 15
Patrick

5 + 5 + 2 + 3 = 15
5, 10, 13, 15
Joel and Taylor

Figure 2.6   The results of groups sharing their strategies with the class

Bailey's group was among the last to share. She, Anna, and Zena added the 8 + 8 − 1 counting method. As Bailey shared, she said, "Our method is just like Karissa and Bethany's, only we used the minimal collection."

I stopped everything to say, "Wow, Bailey is doing something really important here. She is connecting her ideas with others' ideas, just like mathematicians do." Then I asked what she meant by "minimal collection."

Bailey responded, "You know, fewer parts. We used 8 instead of 4 + 4." She continued, "We could have said 16 minus 1, because the two 8s are 16."

210

215

I asked, "What do others think of that?"

Patrick said, "It's like counting the whole thing as a square minus 1." 220

I grabbed a recording sheet and circled the whole diagram and asked, "Do you mean like this?"

"Yea, because it's a 4-by-4 square with 1 missing in the corner," Patrick responded.

As I reflected on this work, there was plenty of evidence that students 225 think about multiplication as repeated addition. Even though not many skip-counting strategies were shared, I did see many students recording statements like 3, 6, 9, 12, 15; and 5, 10, 15; as well as 2, 4, 6, 8, 10, 12, 14, and 15. I wondered if another context or different numbers might encourage more students to see multiplication as an area. Do students see 230 the relationships between repeated addition, skip counting, and the area models? What are students thinking about Bailey's notion that there are "minimal" or simplified versions of these expressions? Perhaps another task would yield more information.

C A S E 10

Candy canes in packages

Janine
GRADE 4, DECEMBER

I sat with three girls today as they tried to tackle the following problem: 235

? There are 609 students at the school. How much would it cost to buy each one a candy cane? Candy canes are sold in packages of 6 for $ .29.

I have been trying to make the rounds and sit with a different group each day. It's interesting to see who has the concepts, who sits back, who 240 leads the discussion, who is totally lost, which ones listen to each other, and which ones hear only their own voice.

The threesome that I sat with today is a new grouping. They have never worked together before, but they seemed to click on this problem.

Janine

Each started out working on her own for a few minutes, and they began talking. Almost immediately the three decided that the problem had something to do with the 6 times tables—and that they had to go pretty far up the table to get to where they wanted to be. They started 6, 12, 18, 24, 30, and soon realized that there had to be a faster way.

Letitia, who grasps concepts pretty quickly, suggested that they should do 90 × 6 because, she figured out, that would be 540. Wow! Good for her, I thought. We have been working on multiplying numbers by multiples of 10, so I guess this clicked for her: $6 × 9 = 54$, so 6 × 90 would equal 540. I was hoping she would take it one step further and see that 6 × 100 would be 600, but she stopped there and neither of the other two saw this either. Maybe this is because, when studying the 6 tables in third grade, they only went up to 6 × 9.

From 540 they decided that they had to add up by 6s to get to 609. This is where keeping track of their numbers became *very* difficult. Letitia, after some thought, said that 540 + 10 more would equal 600. One of the others said that 540 + 10 is equal to 550 and not 600. Letitia struggled to explain. She had the idea that 10 groups of 6 would get her to 600, but she kept confusing *10* and *10 groups of 6*. I could see her struggling to keep track of her thoughts; I could see her "getting it" and then having it fly out of her mind. She knew that 10 was important, but couldn't hold onto the idea that it wasn't 10 but *10 groups of 6* she was thinking about.

To help her out a little, I asked how many more she needed to get to 600 from 540. She answered 60. "Oh yeah—60 is 10 groups of 6!" She would grasp this idea for a while and then lose it again. She was really trying hard to hold onto the meaning of this 10!

So now they had 90 packages and 10 packages for a total of 600 candy canes. They knew they needed 9 more candy canes. One more package would bring them to 606, but they still needed 3 more. Could they buy 3 separately? No, they came in boxes of 6. If they bought another box, they would have 3 extra. What would they do with them? Natalia said, "Let's just eat them! We did the shopping. We deserve a prize!" All happily agreed that they would eat the 3 extras themselves.

Finally the group established that they had to buy 90 + 10 + 2 packages of candy canes. Because they didn't know how to multiply 102 × $ .29, they decided to do it with the calculator. Their answer came out 2958, which they reasoned would be $29.58.

CASE 11

How do kids think about division?

GRADES 3 AND 4, OCTOBER

In the past I have begun the year by having kids do projects, such as making maps or building pendulums, that integrate math topics with other areas of the curriculum. I did this because I wanted to see what ideas kids were thinking about before I began pursuing my own agenda. Kids were certainly invested and interested in the projects, but the specific math topics that I could expect to be covered were unpredictable. Although I love to teach math this way, and there is great potential in this approach, I decided instead to begin this year by focusing on the four operations. I shifted away from a project-based math curriculum so I could study the mathematics the children were doing. I chose to give my own creative ideas a rest to investigate the children's ideas more closely.

As I discussed my plan with a colleague, she seemed reassured by this steady, reliable way of thinking about math. Last year she clearly didn't trust that kids would get enough exposure to the four basic operations while pursuing big, in-depth projects. So she was feeling comforted— until I said I was particularly interested in learning how my eight-, nine-, and ten-year-old students thought about division. This horrified her, because she believes that children need to be taught the operations in a certain order. In her mind, first comes addition, then multiplication, then subtraction, then division.

My initial idea was just to expose kids to division problems early in their experience with numbers so that the process would be familiar when they came to the numbers that themselves implied division— decimals and fractions. But, through my classroom research, I'm learning much more about how kids think about division, what they call division, and how they define division. Much of this learning comes from my observations of their written work.

Each week I have given the students story problems that I considered to be division problems, problems I myself would solve by using

285

290

295

300

305

310

division. Here are some examples of the problems and some kids' responses to them.

 Jesse has 24 shirts. If he puts 8 of them in each drawer, how many drawers does he use?

Vanessa wrote: $24 - 8 = 16$, $16 - 8 = 8$, $8 - 8 = 0$, and then wrote 3 for the answer.

If Jeremy needs to buy 36 cans of seltzer water for his family and they come in packs of 6, how many packs should he buy?

This time Vanessa wrote: $6 + 6 = 12$, $12 + 12 = 24$, $24 + 6 = 30$, $30 + 6 = 36$. I still need to ask her how many packs that gives her. But what made her add this time and subtract last time?

Other students use these same methods. Is it significant that sometimes they add and sometimes they subtract? What are their choices based on? I thought the problems about Jesse's shirts and the six-packs of seltzer water were the same kind of problem, and yet students treated them differently. On reflection, I wonder if the total number (24 or 36 in this case) affects how kids approach the problem. If the total number is a familiar one, do they subtract (until they get zero), and if the number is less familiar, do they add, building up to the number, as Vanessa did for the second problem?

 Joni wants to build some bookshelves for her friends and family. If she bought 36 boards and she needs 4 boards for each bookshelf, how many bookshelves is she going to make?

Cory had clearly tried approaching this problem more than one way. His paper was filled with tally marks, which seemed to be one way he was thinking about it, while above the problem he had written $2 \div 36 = 28 \div 2 = 14$. I decided to ask him about his thinking. I assumed he meant $36 \div 2 = 28$, but I wasn't sure how he got the 28. I wanted to find out how he was really thinking about the problem instead of making assumptions.

Cory told me, "I thought it was times." Then he reread the problem aloud. "See, that's why I changed it to divided by. If it was 4 divided by, I would probably use 2 first so it would be easier. First I would do 2 divided by 36, and that equals 28, and 2 divided by 28 equals 14, so that's how I came up with 14. Because I knew divided by is half of whatever the number is, like 2 divided by 100 is 50."

Georgia

I asked Cory, "Does that mean that 28 is half of 36?"

"Yes," he said, "because I know half of 30 is . . . wait a second . . . no, that isn't right. It would be 15 plus another 3, that's probably 18 and divided by that, which is 9."

Cory knew that 36 is made up of 30 and 6, and half of 30 is 15, and half of 6 is 3. Then he knew that 15 plus 3 is 18. He understands division in terms of halving, as he clearly states: "Divided by is half of whatever the number is." Halving is also implicit in his comment, "That's probably 18 and divided by that, which is 9"; he doesn't even have to say he halved it. And he knows that dividing by 4 is like halving twice. What about division that isn't based on half? Would that be division to him? What will happen when he has to divide by 3?

> **?** You go into a pet store that sells mice. There are 48 mouse legs. How many mice are there?

Matthew organized his work beautifully. He wrote a key (m = mice, l = legs) and put his numbers in columns.

1 m	4 l
2 m	8 l
3 m	12 l
4 m	16 l
5 m	20 l
6 m	24 l
7 m	28 l
8 m	32 l
9 m	36 l
10 m	40 l
11 m	44 l
12 m	48 l

Then in a neat box he wrote, "12 m × 4 l = 48 l." Above the box he wrote the number 12. What does this say about Matthew's understanding of division? He knows that 12 is the answer, but he feels satisfied with a multiplication number sentence in which the answer is *part* of the problem rather than the *answer* to the problem. He knows how to find the answer, but instead of the number sentence I had expected, $48 \div 4 = 12$, he wrote a multiplication number sentence.

Making Meaning for Operations

During a conversation with classmates about a similar problem, Matthew said, "This is another division problem. It's 63 divided by 9. What number times 9 is 63? Seven." When I asked him to explain what there was about the problem that made it a division problem, he said, "I don't know, but it is. But my thinking is multiplication." 385

What does this say about kids' understanding of division if they use all the operations *except* division? As I look at how kids think about division, and how I had initially hoped that the work would help kids with fractions, I wonder in what way the two topics are connected. Do kids bump up against the same ideas in both division and fraction work? What does this say about how kids think about wholes and parts? 390

C A S E 12

Are these kids or seeds?

Melinda
GRADE 2, NOVEMBER

On Halloween I had my second graders work on this word problem:

 6 children are sharing 45 roasted pumpkin seeds. They want to share them as evenly as possible. How many will they each get? 395

I have to say first that I was really amazed and impressed with the industry and confidence with which the children approached the problem. Almost everyone got right to work and seemed to be engaged. Here are some things that seemed interesting to me. 400

Maria, Nikita, and Su-Yin worked together. They each got 45 Multilink™ cubes and snapped them together in a row. Su-Yin's initial strategy involved taking one cube off her collection of 45 so that she would have an even number left. When I asked her why she wanted an even number, she said so she could divide it in half. I asked her why she wanted to divide it in half, and what she planned to do next. She said she 405 didn't know. I wondered whether she had some idea that she might be able to split her two even groups into three groups each somehow. On the other hand, maybe dividing something fairly made her think of halves and even numbers, without having any specific thought about needing six groups.

I never did find out, because Nikita and Maria had a different strategy, which Su-Yin adopted. Maria started making 6 piles of cubes, first breaking off a stick of 5 cubes for each. She then gave each pile 2 more, and had 3 cubes left.

I left these three girls for a while and worked with other children. When I returned to them, Maria was working by herself, drawing her 6 piles of 7 cubes, and Nikita and Su-Yin were arguing. Nikita was saying that each child got 7 seeds, and Su-Yin was saying each got 6, and that Nikita was counting a kid as a seed. Su-Yin indicated her 6 piles of cubes and asked me, "Are these kids or seeds?" I asked her what she meant, and she said that Nikita thought that they were all seeds, but that she had made each of her groups by putting a cube to be a kid in the center and then putting seeds around it. Therefore, her groups were 6 seeds and 1 kid each.

I was interested in Su-Yin's plan for representing and solving the problem, and I wondered what she had thought about in the process. I asked her to explain and show me exactly what she had done and thought from the beginning. She said she got 45 cubes, then put the 45 cubes in a big pile and made sure there were 45. I asked her why she had to have 45, and she said, "That's how many seeds there are." She explained then that she wanted to make groups by putting a kid in the middle and putting seeds around it, so she started to take cubes from the 45, and then said, "Oh! I need to get 6 more cubes!" I asked her why, and she said, "Because those *are* seeds!"

My question is, Is this about keeping track of units again? Su-Yin had to keep track of the numbers 45 and 6 from the start of this problem, and eventually there were some 7s and a 3. She had to think not just of the numbers and how they relate to each other, but also what they represent in this problem. I think that her plan to represent a child and then give the child a fair share of cubes representing seeds was a good one.

But was it too much for her to hold onto at once? First she didn't realize that she couldn't take any of the 45 cubes to make children, because those 45 represented the whole collection of seeds. Then, in her representation, she thought each group of 7 cubes showed a child and his or her seeds, still not realizing that "children" couldn't be taken from the "seeds," and that all the cubes had to be counted as seeds in the end. It was a lot to hold onto!

I am also intrigued by the fact that Nikita and Su-Yin were so clear about what they were disagreeing about. Su-Yin's statement that Nikita was turning a kid into a seed showed some clarity about what was going on and where the confusion was, even though it was in fact *she* who had turned a seed into a kid. I also wonder why Nikita was so sure she was right about the problem, the solution, and her representation of them, but could not convince Su-Yin.

Meanwhile, Derrick and William were having an interesting time with the problem. William, who is fairly able but not very confident, said immediately, "I have an idea!" His idea, which he shared with Derrick, was to start with 45 and keep taking off 6s. They did *not* want to use manipulatives or draw pictures. They did use William's plan, and subtracted 6 repeatedly from 45 "in their heads." They ended up with a list of numbers, run together and hard to read:

$$45\ 39\ 33\ 27\ 21\ 15\ 9\ 3$$

William did say that he took out 6s because that was 1 seed for each child. I wasn't sure whether their list of numbers told him how many seeds each child ended up with, but my colleague Lydia was in the room, and she had a conversation with him about it. She later explained to me that he started to divide their list of numbers in a way to show that each time he subtracted 6, he was giving each child 1 seed. However, he made a mistake about where to divide the run-together numerals, and ended up with 6 groups. It didn't bother him that the numbers he created by dividing up his string did not make sense in the context of the problem.

$$\overset{1}{4539}\Big|\overset{2}{33}\Big|2\ \overset{3}{7}\Big|\overset{4}{211}\Big|\overset{5}{59}\Big|\overset{6}{3}$$

Melinda

When I joined William and Derrick, they had their list of numbers and had drawn 6 little bowls with 6 little seeds in each. I asked them what the bowls were and how many seeds they had in their picture. William replied that the bowls were the seeds for each kid. Derrick figured out how many seeds they had drawn by adding 6s, and said there were 36. William agreed. Neither boy seemed bothered by the fact that they had accounted for only 36 seeds, when there were 45 in the problem.

I asked them, "How many seeds would be left then?" They figured out that there would be 9 by counting on from 36 up to 45. When I asked what they could "do" with the extra 9 seeds, they disagreed. William suggested that each child could have one more seed, but Derrick said, "No, there's only enough for one kid. You would need another kid." I asked why, and he said because there was only "one more 6." He decided that maybe one of the existing kids could get 6 more seeds, or 12 total, and that 3 could be thrown out. For some reason, he was unwilling to divide up a group of 6 seeds in order to give each child one more.

Apparently Derrick convinced William to give one person 12 and everyone else 6 (perhaps because I joked that maybe one of the kids was bossy or bigger or hungrier). When William explained his thinking to the class (I had him put out cubes to show his bowls of seeds), he had a group of 12 and 5 groups of 6. He went back and forth between labeling his groups of 6 as one seed for each kid and as a single kid's share of seeds. I think he was confused because he initially took out groups of 6 with a plan to give one seed in the group to each kid, and to do this as many times as possible, but then began to see those original piles of 6 as the seeds *for* each kid. I wondered why he didn't distribute 6 of the remaining 9 seeds in the end. Why did he stop distributing seeds when each of the 6 kids had 6?

Again, I have questions about how children can keep the "whole" group of seeds in mind while they think of particular ways to divide it

475

480

485

490

495

500

Making Meaning for Operations

into parts. There are many issues for children to sort out: As they start dividing up the whole, what do their groups mean? Are they collections for each child? One seed for each child? Are the children themselves represented in their diagram or model of the problem? Although there were many confusions while these second graders worked on the problem, I have to say that they were remarkably able to make sense of a very complex question.

505

C H A P T E R

3

When dividing doesn't come out evenly

CASE 13	Can you divide 39 into 5?	MaryAnn, Grade 4, April
CASE 14	Can you divide 39 into 5? revisited	MaryAnn, Grade 5, November
CASE 15	7 Brownies, 4 people	Lori, Grade 1, November
CASE 16	Zero is special; zero is nothing	Jayson, Grade 7, September

The action of sharing provides a context in which children can learn about the meaning of division. It also allows them to sort out some of the complexities of dividing whole numbers: What happens when the numbers don't divide evenly? Is it ever possible to divide a greater number into a lesser number? What sense could that possibly have?

In this chapter, we visit the same class twice as students explore what 5 ÷ 39 might mean. In the spring of fourth grade, the students think about the question only in terms of whole numbers. What contexts are modeled by 5 ÷ 39, and what would be the result of dividing 5 by 39? When they return to the question several months later as fifth graders, they are ready to consider their answer in terms of fractions. But their explorations now raise a new set of fascinating questions. As you read about these students' discussions, what ideas about division are highlighted for you? What new ideas must students entertain as they extend their work to the realm of fractions? And what ideas are *you* left to work through for yourself?

Next, we turn to a first-grade class that has been challenged with the problem of sharing 7 brownies among 4 people. As you read about the thinking of these young children, what other ideas about fractions are highlighted?

Finally, we read about seventh graders who use their understanding of whole-number division to make sense of dividing into 0 and dividing by 0. As you read about the thinking of these middle school students, what other ideas about division are highlighted?

After reading the cases, review this introduction and take notes on your thoughts.

C A S E 13

Can you divide 39 into 5?

MaryAnn

GRADE 4, APRIL

This year I came to understand much more deeply what it means to engage my students in discussion of mathematical ideas. I have become convinced that attention to mathematical thinking will serve them much better than exclusively drilling on computational procedures. However, as the metropolitan standardized test approaches, I am concerned. It matters to the lives of these inner-city children that they score well. The test does not assess how thoughtful they are about the meaning of the mathematics they do. Rather, it tests their speed and accuracy on arithmetic facts and procedures—what we've called "mastery" in the past.

For this reason, I decided to dedicate several weeks to the kind of problems they would face on the test. I distributed the textbook I have used in the past and assigned pages of drill. The day we were working on

5

10

Making Meaning for Operations

the "Division with Remainders" page, however, I realized that once we
had entered the realm of ideas, we would never be far away from it. The
session went like this.

TEACHER: Leo, what is problem 9? [*It's such a simple problem, I am almost
not listening to the response.*]

LEO: 5 divided by 39.

The problem on the page reads 39 ÷ 5. Hoping that Leo will correct
himself, I ask him to repeat his statement, but he sticks with the same
response. I ask the class if they agree with Leo, and they all say yes.
Is this important? Should I restate the problem correctly? Are the
children simply being inattentive or does this indicate a deeper lack of
understanding?

TEACHER: What would the answer to the problem 5 divided by 39 look
like? [*All hands go up. I call on Keesha.*]

KEESHA: 7 remainder 4.

TEACHER: If the problem is 5 divided by 39, is 7 remainder 4 the
answer?

The students all say that it is. I wait for a while; we all wait for a while.
The fact that we haven't moved on forces the students to review their
work. They're beginning to realize they can take a risk here and discuss
foggy ideas.

T.C.: The number will be like—I say zero. You can't divide 5 with
a 39 'cause it's a higher number. You can't divide a number
that's lower by one that's higher.

At this point, the rest of the group seems to be neither convinced nor
unconvinced but rather restlessly disinterested. They seem uncomfortable
with my sticking with the same problem when they are all so sure the
answer is 7 r 4. I am uncomfortable, too, and I wonder what they are so
"sure" of.

I have Clarence repeat what T.C. said, and he states it correctly. The
other students all agree that he has verbalized the statement accurately,
but no one seems to have a feeling for what it means, whether it works or
doesn't work, or how it might translate in a context. I sense that they are
thinking only about rules for numbers without making a connection to
what the problem means.

MaryAnn
GRADE 4, APRIL

TEACHER: Is it true that you can't divide a number by a greater number?

ALEJANDRO: Yes, that's true. 5 can't divide by 39. If you had 39 kids and 5 dollars, you can't do that in a fair way. You will give 1 dollar to 5 persons and the other people will be mad.

I'm glad that Alejandro has introduced a context for us to think about. I'm also glad to hear him use the word "fair" and hope that the others will be triggered to think of the "fair shares" we had been studying not so many weeks ago.

DEON: He's right, because the answer will be something about zero 'cause there is no answer for a problem like that.

Well, the kids didn't pick up on fair shares. Now I wonder about Deon's idea that if there is no answer, then the answer is zero. Does zero make sense to him in the problem 5 ÷ 39? Is zero the answer to the problem or does zero mean there are no answers? Is the distinction between the two clear to him or to the others?

JACKSON: You cannot do 5 divided by 39 because on a calculator it won't work out. It will come out to be a number in the minus. It will be . . . .

Jackson's voice drops and then he stops. It seems that everyone is confused and few have any sense of the difference between 39 ÷ 5 and 5 ÷ 39. How could they have sat for days, apparently comfortably, doing whole pages of these traditional exercises? What has happened to all our thinking and discussing and the conclusions that we drew when we worked on fractions? What is their sense about the numbers here? I ask whether it might help to think of another context. Deon is tentative but offers one.

DEON: Well, 5 people and 39 desks. . . . [*He's not sure how to go on.*]

CYNTHIA: What T.C. said is true. If there were 39 principals and I had 5 pieces of candy to give them, then only 5 principals could have a piece. The other 34 would be mad at me and I would lose my job.

As I'm trying to sort out why Cynthia is subtracting, I'm also wondering about whether I should introduce another context. What if

Making Meaning for Operations

there were 39 principals and 5 pizzas? Would that context help them to think in terms of fractions? What if I made the problem simpler: 1 pizza and 4 kids? I suggest both examples, but the children don't pursue them.

SHANNON: 5 divided by 39 really gets me confused. I can't see it in
            my mind.   85

Shannon goes to the board. I ask her to write 5 divided by 39, but she writes 39 ÷ 5. She just doesn't want to confront what seems so foreign to her. She keeps writing 39 ÷ 5 no matter how many times we rephrase the problem. She says that she doesn't want to stretch any more and asks to   90
sit down. It's time to end the lesson.

Throughout today's class, many children just couldn't see that 39 ÷ 5 and 5 ÷ 39 model two different situations. Those who could see the difference decided that 5 could not be divided by 39 because there was no fair way to do it. I wasn't sure what to do. Is this something to follow   95
up tomorrow, or should I continue with my agenda of preparing for the metropolitan exam?

C A S E   **14**

Can you divide 39 into 5? revisited

MaryAnn
GRADE 5, NOVEMBER

This year I am in the fortunate position to have moved up a grade, together with my class. That is, the children I had last year in fourth grade are with me again this year as fifth graders. I am very pleased.   100
They are delightful children, a pleasure to be with two years in a row. At the beginning of the year, we had much less work to do to establish norms of being in class together; there was already a sense of community among us. The several children who were new needed a couple of weeks to catch on, but they had good models in their classmates. This   105
is especially helpful since we have some difficult circumstances to work with. For example, my class of 28 children is very unbalanced by gender:

MaryAnn

GRADE 5, NOVEMBER

21 boys and 7 girls. If I had been meeting this group for the first time, we would have had to do a lot of work to make sure that the girls had a voice in the class. I still have to be careful, but in general the girls feel at ease, even though they are so much in the minority.

In math class, most of the kids already know what it means to have a mathematical discussion. And it's fascinating to me to have the opportunity to see how ideas develop from one year to the next.

In November we were working on division. We had just finished a few sessions in which we looked at remainders in different contexts and saw them expressed as decimals or fractions. We also considered contexts in which it made sense to round up or down to the next whole number. Now I wanted to explore an extension: situations in which there are more sharers than the number of items to be shared.

I asked the class to think about 3 kids sharing 2 candy bars. Just as the discussion began, Leo looked puzzled and recalled a conversation that we had last year. He claimed that the class reached the conclusion that we couldn't divide a larger number into a smaller number. As he presented the facts of last year's discussion, others began to nod. They were recalling the conversation and the contexts we used in our $5 \div 39$ controversy. Now they were looking at me accusingly. How could I be asking them to divide 2 candy bars among 3 kids if we already "knew" that we couldn't do it?

This situation made me wonder about the wisdom of leaving students in the middle of a misunderstanding. Would they have understood any more if last year I had told them that we *can* divide 39 into 5? Would they have been as invested in today's discussion? Were they now having an intuitive sense that we *could* do it? Although it was not my planned entry point into this new division idea—I had intended to work with easier numbers—we stuck with $5 \div 39$ because the class had an investment in it. I began by writing on the board $5 \div 39$ and $39 \div 5$.

ANTHONY: I think that $39 \div 5$ will be 7 remainder 4, but I think that $5 \div 39$ will make a decimal number.

I wonder if he is thinking of a number less than 1, and I wonder why he went to a decimal rather than a fraction. I was surprised because fractions "look" more like "less than 1" than decimals do—at least they do to me.

JACKSON: I think that you will end up with a fraction of a number because, well, because, 5 and 39—you can't divide 5 by 39 equally. I think it's going to be a number below 0.

145

I think that Jackson is headed in the right direction, especially when he says "a fraction *of* a number." (Am I just hoping that the number is 1?)

I wonder aloud about the answer being a fraction, and then about the idea that it would be below 0. I believe that if I had stuck with my original 2 ÷ 3 problem in the candy-bar context, this might have been easier to visualize. But I don't know if the students would have been so invested; they have a sense of ownership over the problems involving 5 and 39.

150

ALEJANDRO: I agree with Anthony but not with Jackson. We had some story problems where the answers were decimals but they were not below 0. I think we could say that 39 ÷ 5 could be a decimal number. [*He goes to the board and shows how he solved for a quotient of 7.8.*] I think that this is what Anthony means.

155

Anthony says that this is *not* what he means, but that he doesn't feel ready yet to explain. Alejandro used decimals to solve 39 ÷ 5, but did not try 5 ÷ 39 and did not address the crucial point of using a decimal to name a number less than 1. I'm pretty sure that this is where Anthony's going, but I respect his decision to remain quiet for now.

160

DARRELL: I think 39 can't go into 5. I mean, it can go into it, but it's going to be a fraction, it's got to be a fraction. A larger number into a smaller number—5 can go into 39, but there's a remainder. No, it's not a remainder; it's not a number.

165

I really don't get what Darrell is saying. Does he think that fractions or decimals are only remainders? Why does he think that it's "not a number"?

170

GREG: I agree with Anthony and with Jackson because 39 divided by 5, no, 5 divided by 39. . . .

Greg repeats the two problems four or five times. There's something that he's trying to sort out. However, the numbers removed from context clearly have little meaning for him.

175

MaryAnn

GRADE 5, NOVEMBER

LEO: 5 divided by 39 is going to be a smaller number. You have
            39 people and 5 candies.

I stop to ask the class which one of the notations, 39 ÷ 5 or 5 ÷ 39,
expresses Leo's story. I want to see if we are at least making a connection
between the context and the correct notation. Most of the students didn't
get that last year.

Mitchell chooses the correct notation and explains that the answer
would be pieces of candy bars. (YES!)

MITCHELL: So, if each kid was going to get equal shares, they would
            have to cut the 5 candy bars into little equal pieces.

TEACHER: Can you name those equal pieces?

MITCHELL: They might be candy bars.

TEACHER: Can you name the fraction that they might be?

MITCHELL: [*After a long pause*] They wouldn't be able to do it.

DARN! We stop now to take a class poll. How many people think
that you can do the problem 5 ÷ 39? How many think no, you can't? The
results: yes, 13; no, 15.

After a pause, Leo says that he wants to change his no to a yes. He
starts to explain that you cut each bar into 7 equal pieces, and then asks if
he can go to the board. He draws circles to show the 39 people and then
draws five rectangles for the 5 candy bars. He shows that partitioning
2 candy bars into sevenths will yield 14 pieces and then, without making
the lines, indicates that partitioning 4 candy bars will produce 28 pieces.
He pauses and sees then that the fifth candy bar will give him a total of
35 pieces. He then draws in lines to show that he has cut the last bar into
11 pieces. Now he's satisfied because he has a total of 39 pieces.

Cynthia quickly responds that this representation couldn't be
correct because it isn't equal shares. She seems sure of it. There are

four rectangles with sevenths and only one with elevenths. "That's a
problem," she says.

As Cynthia talks, Tori goes to the board and points to the elevenths.

TORI: Nobody would want one of these small pieces. There's
           something about Leo's solution that feels right, but
           something also seems wrong.

MARIBEL: I think that Leo is on the right track because each person
           would only get a really small piece, not anywhere like a
           whole candy bar. But Tori is right, too, because the shares
           that he drew aren't the same for each person.

LAILA: If I cut each of the 5 candy bars into 39 pieces and then give
           each kid one piece from each candy bar, you could have each
           kid have $\frac{5}{39}$ of a candy bar.

Laila wants to go to the board and draw hers. She draws 5 rectangles
divided up into 39 equal boxes. She is displaying some confidence and
some clear mathematical thinking that I have not seen before.

ANTHONY: I think the same thing, that each person will get one piece
           from the first candy bar and one piece from the second and
           then from each one after that and will end up with 5 little
           pieces, so $\frac{5}{39}$.

ALEJANDRO: I was thinking that if you wanted you could take 5 from
           each candy bar over and over again until you were done, but
           I think that I know that because of the drawing Laila did.

Alejandro has learned something from the discussion; Laila's work
made an impact on him. I'm glad to hear him acknowledge her.

We ended the discussion right there, but continued a few days later.
Since I happened to have three visitors on that day (three colleagues from
the professional development project I'm in), I divided the class into
four groups. Each group worked with an adult to come up with a way to
show 5 ÷ 39. Time passed very quickly and we had little time for groups
to report back to the whole class.

Leo and Cynthia said that they didn't really have a name for their
solution, but they were ready to defend their thinking. Cynthia went to
the board and drew a diagram that showed how they divided 5 candy
bars for 39 people (see next page).

It was time to end class. Time was short and, even though all the groups had worked hard, I think we were all feeling unsatisfied. Jackson looked at Cynthia's diagram and asked what 40 fortieths has to do with $5 \div 39$. I asked the students to think about that for their homework.

When we returned to the problem the next day, people were feeling refreshed again, ready to take on Cynthia's diagram. While her drawing helped some of the students picture the problem, it raised even more questions:

What is the last piece called? Is it $\frac{1}{8}$ or $\frac{1}{40}$?

What's the whole?

What happens if the last piece is divided into 39 pieces? What if it is divided into 40 pieces?

Do we know what $\frac{5}{39}$ means? Is "slightly more than $\frac{1}{8}$" a better answer than $\frac{5}{39}$ because it's clearer, even though it's less exact? What about $\frac{1}{8}$ and $\frac{1}{39}$ of $\frac{1}{8}$? What about $\frac{1}{8}$ and $\frac{1}{39}$ of $\frac{1}{40}$? When we say $\frac{1}{8}$, it's $\frac{1}{8}$ of what? When we say $\frac{1}{40}$, it's $\frac{1}{40}$ of what? If we cut the last piece into fortieths, each person gets $\frac{1}{8}$ plus $\frac{1}{40}$ of $\frac{1}{8}$. What happens to the extra fortieth? Do we keep on dividing it? (This is where we discussed the "piece," the "sliver," and the "crumb.")

Some of these questions I need to sort out for myself.

7 Brownies, 4 People

Lori

I am participating in a seminar called *Making Meaning for Operations*. As an assignment, we were asked to present to our students the following problem:

> **?** I have 7 brownies and I want to share them among my 4 friends. How many brownies would each friend get?

265

At our next seminar meeting, we will share how our class approached and solved the problem. It will be a very interesting conversation, because our seminar includes teachers from pre-kindergarten through eighth grade. Following is an account of the response from my class.

270

My students have listened to, interpreted, and solved many story problems. However, this problem was different from the combining and separating situations they were familiar with. This was a sharing situation.

I first attempted to do the activity as a whole class, but the students were baffled and I was besieged with questions. My responses were insufficient, and more questions followed. I felt that I could not attend to each student's questions as I usually do. I couldn't give my focused attention to a single student when twenty others were approaching me at once.

275

280

So, I decided to make the "7 Brownies, 4 People" a new center activity that students would circulate through, along with few other math center activities already familiar to the class. This gave me the opportunity to have in-depth conversations with a few students at a time. Only then was I able to listen, to question, and to challenge each student's mathematical thinking.

285

Lori

Independently, many students came up with one of two different solutions. Either they gave 1 brownie to each person and had 3 brownies left, or they gave 2 brownies to each person, giving 1 more brownie than was available. Two conversations captured the essence of the dilemma confronting my students. Although most students were unable to articulate it so clearly, it is interesting that some could.

TEACHER:	Mathew, how many brownies did each person get?
MATHEW:	I gave 8 brownies away.
TEACHER:	Do you have 8 brownies to give away?
MATHEW:	No.
TEACHER:	No, then how many brownies do you have to give away?
MATHEW:	7.
TEACHER:	So, how many brownies would each person get?
DIANE:	It is going to be hard, because 7 is not an equal number . . . because 7 is an odd number.
TEACHER:	So then what could we do?
DIANE:	One kid has to get less than the others.
TEACHER:	Is there a way that each kid will get the same amount? Think about it. If you want, you could use these papers to represent the brownies.
MATHEW:	I know, I would have to split one up.
DIANE:	Oh, that's a good idea.
MATHEW:	I would give them all 1 brownie, and then I would cut one in half.

Lori

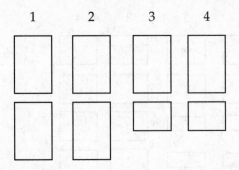

Mathew's solution was the most common response to my challenge. He first gave each person 1 brownie; then he gave another brownie to the first two people; he split the last brownie into 2 half pieces; the third and fourth person received $1\frac{1}{2}$ brownies.

315

Diane solved it differently. "I gave her 2, and him 2, and him 2, and the last person got a big one broken in half, which is like 2.

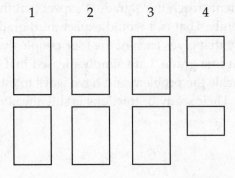

James did it still a different way. He understood that he needed to split the brownies into smaller pieces, but he didn't seem to have a strategy, at least not one he could explain. At first he split the brownies into different-size pieces. Then he started again. This time, he split each brownie into halves. He gave two halves to each person. Then, not knowing what to do next, he split one of the brownies into 4 pieces and gave 2 quarter-pieces to the first and second person, and the remaining 2 brownies to the third and fourth person. In the end, each person received 4 pieces, but two people received 4 half-brownies and the other two received 2 half-brownies and 2 quarter-pieces.

320

325

1   2   3   4

As students each grappled with the problem, they came to understand that the brownies needed to be split. Once they had more pieces to share, they felt that their problem was solved. The students split the brownies in such a way that each person received an equal *number* of pieces, but not necessarily an equal *amount* of brownies.

By the time these students reach third grade, I expect that they will solve the problem differently. That is, I would expect third graders to cut the brownies in a way that gives each of the four people the same amount—$1\frac{3}{4}$ brownies. At first grade, I am simply pleased that my students are willing to tackle the problem and have ways to interpret it that make sense to them. Their study of fractions is still ahead of them.

330

335

CASE 16

Zero is special; zero is nothing

Jayson
GRADE 7, SEPTEMBER

Charlene and I have worked together for several years on district-wide math committees and as district math specialists. Although Charlene has returned to her full-time math teaching at a local junior high school and I am teaching mathematics education at a local university, we continue to work together on examining students' thinking about mathematics.

340

Today, Charlene has invited me to observe her students as they think $\quad$ 345
about dividing a number by zero.

The class is a group of advanced seventh graders who have been
identified as ready to take a beginning algebra class a year or two ahead
of most of their peers at the school. They have been working on how
rates of change, such as $3 per hour or 5 cookies per person, show up on $\quad$ 350
a graphical representation as the slope of a line; for example, for $3 per
hour, the graph "rises" vertically 3 units every time you move 1 unit to
the right; or, as the students would describe it, the ratio $\frac{rise}{run}$ is $\frac{3}{1}$.

Charlene wants students to connect the previous images they have
developed about fractions, ratio, and division to the new images they are $\quad$ 355
developing about rates of change and slope. As she has been thinking
about how to help students interpret the ratio $\frac{rise}{run}$ when the "rise" is 0
or the "run" is 0, she has decided that she first needs to know how they
think about fractions when either the numerator or denominator is 0.
Do they know that when the numerator is equal to 0, the fraction is equal $\quad$ 360
to 0, but when the denominator is equal to 0, the fraction is undefined?
Do they know that when both the numerator and denominator are equal
to 0, here, too, the fraction is undefined? If not, what do they think about
the meaning of such fractions?

To get at students' initial thinking about such fractions, Charlene and $\quad$ 365
I devised five questions for students to answer individually. They are
to be prepared to explain their reasoning to their peers, using pictures,
diagrams, or stories to justify their answers. After recording their initial
ideas, the students will get together in groups to compare answers and
try to reach consensus. They will also need to decide how they will try $\quad$ 370
convincing other members of the class that their answers are correct.

These were the five questions:

1. $\frac{0}{7} = ?$
2. $\frac{7}{0} = ?$
3. If $\frac{x}{9} = 0$, then $x = ?$ $\quad$ 375
4. If $\frac{9}{x} = 0$, then $x = ?$
5. If $x = 0$, then $\frac{x}{x} = ?$

As the students went to work recording their answers and their
ways of thinking about the problems, Charlene and I wandered around
the classroom noting their initial responses. Most students had quickly $\quad$ 380

written 0 as the answer to all five problems and were now going back to
write a reason for each solution. I noticed that as some students thought
more about the problems, they changed some of their answers. For
example, although Tricia kept her answer of 0 for question 1, she changed
question 2 to read $\frac{7}{0} = 7$. To support her answers, Tricia wrote that the
answer to question 1 was 0 because "you can't give 0 things to 7 people."
She had drawn a picture of 7 people with nothing to distribute to them.
For question 2 she wrote, "You can give 7 things to 0 people." She seemed
to be trying to illustrate the action of distributing objects to people while
focusing on the number of objects in her hand.

Brandon had also written 7 for the answer to question 2. To justify his
answer he wrote, "It is right because if you divide 7 crayons by 0 people,
you still have 7 crayons left." Both Brandon and Tricia seemed to be
confused by the actions required by their interpretations of the division
problems, and were left trying to decide what to do with the 7 leftover
objects.

Other students had given non-zero answers to some of the other
questions. For example, on question 5 Tyler had written $\frac{3}{3} = 1$, $\frac{2}{2} = 1$,
$\frac{1}{1} = 1$, $\frac{0}{0} = 1$ and then added the words "zero can go into itself once." For
question 4 Jessica wrote: "If $\frac{9}{x} = 0$, then $x = 10$" and her justification was
that $\frac{10}{10} = 1$, so $\frac{9}{10} = 0$.

Most students, however, continued to believe that 0 was the answer
to all five questions, although they supported their answers in a variety
of ways. I noted later that their justification for question 2 often mirrored
their response to question 1, as if they saw no difference between the two
problems. Some of their initial reasoning about the questions included the
following statements.

Ashley

Question 1: "Because if you split 0 up into 7 parts it is still 0."

Question 2: "Because it's just saying that there's 0 groups of 7
and that means there are not even any groups."

Cameron

Question 1: "There are no pieces of a 7 piece pie, nothing
leaves 0."

Question 2: "You can't have 7 pieces of nothing."

Making Meaning for Operations

Cameron added the following illustrations to support his written responses:

Ryan

Question 1: "If there are 0 cookies for 7 people, no one gets any cookies."

Question 2: "If there are 7 cookies and 0 people, no one gets any cookies."

Brindi

Question 1: "When you have 7 pieces of pie, and there is nobody there, then nobody has pie."

Question 2: "No pie, nobody gets pie."

While Ryan, Brindi, and others had tried to think about division in terms of distributing cookies or pieces of pie to their friends, Mark and Adam were using other images of division to support their answers.

Mark

Question 1: "$\frac{1}{7}$ is one seventh. $\frac{0}{7}$ is zero sevenths. If you have 0 of something you have nothing."

Question 2: "Seven zeros is nothing. $0 + 0 + 0 + 0 + 0 + 0 + 0 = 0$. You can't divide by 0."

Adam

Question 1: "There isn't a 7 in 0."

Question 2: "No 0 in 7."

Meanwhile, Kym had patiently written the same explanation on each answer, finally writing the statement with all capitals for emphasis, "ANYTHING MULTIPLIED OR DIVIDED WITH 0 EQUALS 0!"

As students moved into groups to discuss the problems, one girl confidently announced to her group members, "Well the answer is always 0, isn't it?"

Charlene began working with Ryan, Brandon, Jacob, and Hayley. Hayley was sure that the answer to all five questions was 0, since she had "turned the problem around on all of them—like on question 2 instead of $\frac{0}{7}$ I did $0 \cdot 7 = 0$." The group was convinced that the second division problem, which they had recorded as $\frac{7}{0} = 0$ could also be "turned around" and written as the multiplication problem $0 \cdot 7 = 0$.

Since no one in the group seemed to object to this interpretation, Charlene decided to point out a concern she had. "It looks like you turned the first division problem into multiplication differently than you did the second one. I agree that since $\frac{9}{3} = 3$, I can write the related multiplication $3 \cdot 3 = 9$, but I'm not sure that is what you did on both of these problems. Why don't you look at that again."

As Charlene moved on to another group, I stayed to observe what would happen. Hayley spoke as she wrote, "Oh yeah, the second one should be $0 \cdot 0 = 7$." It took awhile for the implications of this last statement to sink in. "But that's impossible," Jacob said. At this point he picked up his calculator and entered $7 \div 0$ and pointed out the error message that appeared. "The problem doesn't make sense." Jacob crossed out the 0 he had written on his paper and wrote "impossible" instead.

As I wandered over to another group, I heard an argument over whether 7 cookies divided among 0 groups meant you had 7 cookies left, so $\frac{7}{0} = 7$, or did it mean each person gets 0 cookies because there were no groups to give them to, so $\frac{7}{0} = 0$. The voices arguing for "no groups, no cookies" seemed to be winning the debate, but before it could be resolved, Charlene was calling the class back together for sharing.

The class discussion quickly separated into two opposing sides, one side convinced that $\frac{7}{0} = 0$, and the other side convinced that this division was impossible to do. Hayley and Jacob started the class discussion using their "related multiplication fact" argument that if $\frac{7}{0} = 0$, then that would imply that $0 \cdot 0 = 7$. They also pointed out the error message on the calculator.

Cameron led the opposition camp. "We have all been told that 0 is a 'special' number," Cameron said, making quote marks in the air with his fingers to emphasize the word *special*. "Like 0 isn't positive or negative, and 0 isn't prime or not prime, and 0 isn't even or odd."

Benji objected to this last statement, saying that 0 was even, but Charlene wisely deferred that debate until another day.

Cameron continued, "Zero does special things. Like when you add with it, nothing changes, and when you multiply by it, you always get 0 instead of something else. Zero doesn't follow rules, and other strategies don't work for it. It has to be 0 because 0 groups of 7 is 0 and 7 groups of 0 is 0. It's a special number and we have to treat it differently."

Tyler looked very thoughtful as he countered Cameron's argument in favor of Hayley's. "If something is divided by 0 . . . then that can't equal anything." Tyler wrote $7 \div 0 =$ *some answer* on the board. Then he wrote *some answer* $\times 0 = 7$. "And," said Tyler, "no number works for *some answer*."

On the opposing side, Joey came to Cameron's support by focusing on the calculator issue. "Calculators have a problem with dividing by 0 because 0 isn't a number, and the calculator can't deal with nothing."

Cameron added to the calculator argument. "Calculators don't have a mind to work around abstract ideas like dividing by 0. The calculator can't divide by something that's not there."

Ashley also sided with Joey and Cameron: "I think zero is a placeholder. It's something that people use to represent nothing." Ashley had been testing out questions 1 and 2 on her calculator. "When I go 0 divided by 7, I get 0, but when I go 7 divided by 0, I get *error*. It matters where you put the something and the nothing."

Renee turned the conversation back to Hayley and Tyler's argument. "It's like fact families," she said as she wrote the following on the board:

$$3 \times 4 = 12 \quad 12 \div 4 = 3 \quad 4 \times 3 = 12 \quad 12 \div 3 = 4$$

"That's a fact family." Then she wrote the following:

$$0 \times 7 = 0 \quad 0 \div 7 = 0 \quad 7 \times 0 = 0 \quad 0 \div 0 = 7$$

Renee concluded, "That last one's impossible."

Cameron countered, "Fact families are a theory that don't work for 0. Zero is special because everything else represents something and 0 represents nothing." Cameron produced his own "fact family":

$$0 \times 7 = 0 \quad 0 \div 7 = 0 \quad 7 \times 0 = 0 \quad 7 \div 0 = 0$$

Jacob tried to get Cameron to see the implications of his previous argument: "It's impossible for 0×0 to equal something like 7, and that's what you're saying when you write $7 \div 0 = 0$."

Cameron replied, "No, I'm saying $7 \div 0$ doesn't equal anything, so it's zero."

At this point Charlene asked Cameron, "So are you saying that the problem $7 \div 0$ has no solution?" I saw what Charlene was getting at. I, too, wondered if Cameron was using zero to indicate that there was no solution, since in Cameron's mind *zero* is *nothing*.

I slipped quietly out of the classroom as Charlene turned the conversation to slopes of lines where either the "rise" or "run" is 0. As I walked to my car, I wondered about the issues students had raised today through their comments about zero.

Does the belief that zero is "special" or that zero is "nothing" get in the way of seeing zero as a *number*? Do misconceptions about the role that numbers play in multiplication and division (e.g., number of groups, number of objects in each group) prevent students from making sense of division by 0? Do these students see division in two different ways, both as distributing objects to groups (partitive division) and measuring out groups of a certain size (measurement division)? What images might these two different interpretations provide?

I also wondered why their recent work with slopes and rates of change had not entered into the students' conversations. What new images of division by zero might come to mind as Charlene asks students to interpret slopes where the "rise" or the "run" is 0? What would have happened if these students had used images of rate, ratio, or slope to justify their thinking?

As a secondary math teacher, I know that each time we enlarge the number system—from counting numbers, to integers, to fractions, and so forth—we have to renegotiate the meaning of addition, subtraction, multiplication and division. That is, what images of operations still hold true, and what images need to be extended or modified? I had never considered, however, that this renegotiation of meaning of operations has to take place when we enlarge the number system from the set of counting (or natural) numbers to the set of whole numbers. What a difference including zero as a *number* has on our understanding of operations. Do we ever give students an opportunity to make sense of 0 as a number? Have I?

CHAPTER
4

Greater than, less than, equal to

CASE 17	Which is greater? How do you know?	*Faith, Grade 4, May*
CASE 18	Discovering common denominators	*Nelly, Grade 4, March*
CASE 19	Equivalent fractions	*Malik, Grade 5, April*
CASE 20	Today's number is 1	*Zura, Grade 4, March*
CASE 21	Fraction flags	*Kate, Grade 2, March*

The first two chapters of this casebook showed that students first encounter number through counting, and that they can develop initial meaning for the operations as they solve problems by counting. The third chapter showed that the operation of division, along with situations such as sharing, which are modeled by division, introduce a new kind of number, called fractions, that can fall between the counting numbers. There are many things to learn about fractions, including how they are written with two numbers to represent a single quantity.

In this chapter, we encounter students who are working to understand how the two numbers that make up a fraction (the numerator and denominator) together determine the size of the fraction. Using diagrams and reasoning about what the numerator and denominator represent, the students determine which of two fractions is greater. We also find students who explain how two different fractions can actually be the same size, that is, how two fractions can be equivalent.

As you read the cases, take notes on the ways different students determine which of two fractions is greater, and how they know that two fractions are equivalent. Are any of these ideas new to you? What other ways do you have to compare fractions?

C A S E   17

Which is greater? How do you know?

Faith

GRADE 4, MAY

Toward the end of our unit on fractions, my students placed 50 fractions on a number line. As they worked on this task, I told them to be aware of their thinking as they decided which of two fractions is greater so that we could discuss their thinking later.

A few days after this activity, I wrote the following on chart paper to launch our discussion:

Which is greater, $\frac{1}{2}$ or $\frac{2}{3}$?

HARRY: Two-thirds is greater because $\frac{1}{2}$ is only half, and $\frac{2}{3}$ is more than $\frac{1}{2}$. You can see it if you make two squares and split one in half and the other one in thirds.

Making Meaning for Operations

Faith

TEACHER: What are you comparing in these two models?

HARRY: The parts that are shaded in. Two-thirds is greater than one-half.

TEACHER: Any other ways of thinking about these two fractions:

ANNIE: In my mind, I see two circles, one split in thirds and the other in two halves. I compare the parts that are left, you know, the parts not shaded in. One-third is smaller than one-half, so two-thirds is greater than one-half.

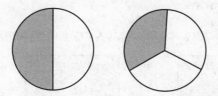

TEACHER: Are there any other ways of thinking about these two fractions?

CHUCK: I compare the fractions this way: When I see $\frac{1}{2}$, I know that 1, the numerator, is half of 2, the denominator. But half of the 3 in $\frac{2}{3}$ is $1\frac{1}{2}$ thirds, so I know that $\frac{2}{3}$ is greater.

I asked Chuck to come to the board to show us.

CHUCK: Well, 1, the numerator, is half of 2, the denominator, so you can write just $\frac{1}{2}$. And one-half of the 3 in $\frac{2}{3}$ is $1\frac{1}{2}$. You could write $1\frac{1}{2}$ over 3 to show it. [*He writes this on the board.*] $1\frac{1}{2}$ over 3 equals $\frac{1}{2}$. So you can see that $\frac{2}{3}$ is bigger than $\frac{1}{2}$, because $1\frac{1}{2}$ is smaller than the numerator, 2.

$$\frac{1\frac{1}{2}}{3}$$

As I looked around the room, I noticed a few students nodding in agreement with Chuck's explanation about the numerator being more than half the denominator. Others were just listening quietly. I decided to go on to another problem.

TEACHER: Which is greater, $\frac{7}{8}$ or $\frac{3}{4}$?

GARY: That's easy; $\frac{7}{8}$ is greater because $\frac{1}{8}$ is less than $\frac{1}{4}$.

Faith

TEACHER: Can you say more?

GARY: You need $\frac{1}{8}$ more to make $\frac{7}{8}$ a whole, and $\frac{1}{4}$ more to make $\frac{3}{4}$ a whole. Since $\frac{1}{8}$ is smaller than $\frac{1}{4}$, then $\frac{7}{8}$ is more.

TEACHER: Do you have a picture in your head? What should I draw?

GARY: Draw two squares, and divide one in eighths and the other in fourths. Shade in 7 of the eighths and 3 of the fourths. When you compare the eighth to the fourth, you can see that one-eighth is smaller, so that means seven-eighths is more than three-fourths.

I drew the following picture according to Gary's directions:

TEACHER: Any other ways of thinking about these fractions:

JESSE: $\frac{6}{8} = \frac{3}{4}$, and one more eighth is more, so $\frac{7}{8}$ is more.

TEACHER: How do you know that $\frac{6}{8} = \frac{3}{4}$?

JESSE: Just look at the picture. You need to take away $\frac{1}{8}$ from the $\frac{1}{4}$ for it to equal $\frac{3}{4}$.

I now asked the class to think about generalizations of how to compare fractions.

TEACHER: Can you talk about how you think about comparing any two fractions? Do you have a rule that helps you?

AMI: Well, when there's a 1 on top in both numbers, then the smaller denominator is bigger.

TEACHER: Can you give me an example?

AMI: Like $\frac{1}{6}$ and $\frac{1}{3}$. They both have 1 for numerators, but the smaller number, the 3, is a bigger piece.

I drew a picture to illustrate what Ami was saying.

Many students agree with Ami's explanation.

TEACHER: Does this work all the time?

MANY
VOICES: It always works when the numerator is 1.

TEACHER: How about when the numerator is greater than 1? 65

REA: When the numerator is more than 1, then the numerator has to be more than half the denominator to be bigger. Like $\frac{2}{8}$ and $\frac{3}{6}$. Three is half of 6, but 2 isn't even close to 8. It would have to be a 4 to be half, so $\frac{3}{6}$ is more.

TEACHER: Would this work all the time? Can we try another example? 70

AMI: Let's try $\frac{6}{8}$ and $\frac{4}{6}$.

She comes to the board and draws the following:

AMI: This one is harder because both numerators are 2 away from the denominators. The half rule doesn't work here.

JESSE: Yeah, but you can tell by looking at whatever's left over. The 75 fraction that has the smaller part left is the greater fraction.

TEACHER: Hmm, can you say more?

JESSE: If the white part on the $\frac{6}{8}$ is smaller than the white part on the $\frac{4}{6}$, then it means $\frac{6}{8}$ is greater.

TEACHER: You're comparing the unshaded parts. How much is 80 not shaded in $\frac{6}{8}$ and $\frac{4}{6}$?

JESSE: In $\frac{6}{8}$, there is $\frac{2}{8}$ not shaded, and for $\frac{4}{6}$, there is $\frac{2}{6}$ not covered. And $\frac{2}{8}$ is smaller than $\frac{2}{6}$, so $\frac{6}{8}$ is greater.

AMI: Yeah, there is more covered on the $\frac{6}{8}$ than the $\frac{4}{6}$, so $\frac{6}{8}$ is greater.   85

TEACHER: So we've seen that the "half rule" doesn't apply to all pairs of fractions.

Previous to this episode, we had talked about comparing any two fractions with 1 as a numerator. Students knew that the fraction with the lesser denominator would be the greater fraction because the piece would   90 be larger. They explained, for example, that if a cake is shared among more people, the piece you get is smaller. Today it was interesting to hear students beginning to articulate other generalizations. For example, if both numerators are the same distance away from the denominators, the "unshaded" part is smaller when the denominator is greater—and that   95 means that the fraction with the greater denominator is more. They also specified how to compare any fraction to $\frac{1}{2}$.

C A S E   18

Discovering common denominators

Nelly

GRADE 4, MARCH

Toward the end of our work on fractions, one of the assessment questions I gave to the class involved comparing $\frac{3}{4}$ and $\frac{5}{6}$. Are they the same size? If not, which is greater? I was puzzled to find that only four   100 students answered the question correctly and gave an explanation that I considered adequate. Some students determined that $\frac{5}{6}$ was greater, but they drew diagrams that were inconclusive. Some students drew accurate pictures but didn't offer an explanation. Some students remembered a conjecture the class had come up with earlier—"the greater   105 the denominator, the smaller the piece"—but misapplied it to this situation, concluding that $\frac{3}{4}$ must be greater. I decided the problem warranted further exploration by the class.

Nelly
GRADE 4, MARCH

Several days later, I reminded the class about the problem and told them, "When I looked over your papers, I noticed that all of you agreed that $\frac{3}{4}$ is not equal to $\frac{5}{6}$, but you were thinking about this problem in many different ways. Also, even though you knew they were not the same amount, you do not agree about which one is more. I think we'll work on this some more today. I'm going to give you some graph paper and have you work together on this problem. I'm sure you will find a lot to talk about in your groups. Share your ideas and see if you can come to some agreement. The graph paper might help you draw your pictures more accurately. Lots of kids said that was a big problem for them." 110 115

I handed out the graph paper, and they got to work very eagerly. As they started, I interrupted briefly to ask, "When you're making your drawings, do the two 'cakes' need to be the same size?" Students nodded, and I asked several of them to restate that principle and suggest how they might make cakes that could be fourths and sixths and were the same size. Someone suggested using a 6-by-6 square, and that idea was adopted by many. 120 125

After students had worked for about 20 minutes drawing on their graph paper and sharing ideas, I invited them to make individual posters. Each poster should explain their ideas and be illustrated by graph-paper drawings.

The next day, we taped the completed posters to the board and gathered for a "mathematics convention." I introduced it by saying, "After your work together, I'm pretty sure that you all agree now that $\frac{5}{6}$ is more than $\frac{3}{4}$. What is your proof that this is true? Let's look at the posters and share ideas. Isn't it fascinating that we can all agree on an answer and still find it so interesting to talk about the different ways we have to prove it?" 130 135

Eli, who had worked so hard on his drawing earlier, delighted in his ability to produce a very accurate drawing with the graph paper. Using a 6-by-6 grid, he drew pictures to show the two fractions (see Figure 4.1). Accompanying his drawing, Eli wrote, "$\frac{5}{6}$ is bigger than $\frac{3}{4}$ because it has more colored in." 140

Figure 4.1   Eli's poster comparing the two fractions

Rebecca's poster is shown in Figure 4.2. Rebecca explained that when she wrote, "$\frac{5}{6}$ has less squares than $\frac{3}{4}$," she meant the numbered squares, those that were *not* included in the amount of cake represented by $\frac{5}{6}$ and $\frac{3}{4}$.

145

Figure 4.2   Rebecca's poster comparing the two fractions

Making Meaning for Operations

Matt's poster (Figure 4.3) illustrated the same principle Rebecca meant to show.

Figure 4.3   Matt's poster comparing the two fractions

It was Bibiana's work, however, that caught the attention of the class and created the most discussion (see Figure 4.4). Bibiana, in her characteristic way, had struggled with her picture until she had finally figured out a way, not just to show that $\frac{5}{6}$ was more, but also to show *how much* more it was. Like many other students, she had worked on a 6-by-6 grid, but as she worked, she began to see the portions as twelfths, not fourths or sixths. She had completed her poster by herself, although she had talked with her groupmates and me about it. She ended up making two representations of the two fractions. The first representation showed the 36 individual squares, and in the second she had labeled the twelfths.

150

155

Figure 4.4   Bibiana's poster comparing the two fractions

Chapter 4

Nelly

Many students seemed quite attentive to the conversation that resulted. Rebecca began, "I can see on your poster that the cakes are the same size. They need to be the same size."

Matt, using his own poster language of "slabs," chimed in. "Yeah, and I see you take out six or nine squares. You take out six squares from the $\frac{5}{6}$ and nine squares from the $\frac{3}{4}$. So it's like $\frac{5}{6}$ is A and $\frac{3}{4}$ is B. There is a slab missing from B and a slab missing from A. One-sixth is less than one-fourth, so you're only taking one-sixth from A but one-fourth from B."

Max, one of the few students who had been able to explain the problem correctly and thoroughly the first day, still got tangled up in the language when he tried to explain today. "When you shade in $\frac{3}{4}$ or $\frac{5}{6}$—the part that's not shaded—if it's bigger than the one that's colored in . . . oh, I can't say it!"

Jillian, who also had been successful the first day, tried to help. "You mean the piece that's not colored in from the three-fourths?" From here, the conversation moved quickly, and there seemed to be a number of students trying to find the words for what they were seeing pretty clearly in Bibiana's poster.

Matt tried again, this time using new language that matched Bibiana's representation instead of his own. "I see what you did. You translated the fourths and sixths into twelfths. Instead of having to compare fourths and sixths, they're both twelfths now. This is a very practical way. I like your way."

I asked, "What do you mean by 'practical,' Matt?"

Rebecca volunteered, "It's easy to understand, and it's simple. It's practical."

Jillian expanded on the idea: "You can really see it. There are nine-twelfths in three-fourths and ten-twelfths in five-sixths."

Bibiana's poster and this conversation had been particularly satisfying. It seemed that all the students had had enough experience with the problem and a chance to draw careful pictures with the graph paper so that Bibiana's discovery of common denominators made some sense to them.

However, as always seems to happen in a classroom, we were not allowed to rest content and free from confusion for long. Kalina presented the last poster, which included her own conjecture:

$\frac{5}{6}$ is greater than $\frac{3}{4}$ because 5 is more than 3 and 6 is more than 4.

As my students puzzled over her idea, I realized we still had a long way to go. Kalina, who usually understands math concepts and had shown particularly strong intuitive understanding of fractions, had drawn some representations in defense of her conjecture. It was as if she had grabbed at an idea that sounded good in words, drawn some pictures, and hoped she had proved something.

I realized I had some more pondering to do myself. I reminded myself that an understanding of these concepts develops slowly over time. Bibiana had given us a clear direction and a sense of satisfaction, but we still had struggles ahead.

C A S E   19

Equivalent fractions

Malik

GRADE 5, APRIL

In one of our class discussions, we had found several fractions equivalent to $\frac{1}{5}$, including $\frac{2}{10}$, $\frac{4}{20}$, and $\frac{8}{40}$. I asked the students what they saw.

Many of the students said the numbers were doubling. We discussed whether or not the fractions, themselves, were doubling. Some of the students answered, yes, they were doubling the fractions.

In order to clarify some vocabulary, I talked about how the numerators and denominators were doubling. Whether the value of the fractions doubled, this was something we'd need to think through.

Macario said that he thought the fraction was still the same but looked different. In order to communicate his reasoning, he drew a diagram.

$\frac{1}{4}$

$\frac{2}{8}$

He pointed out, "When you double the numbers in the fraction, the fraction will still be the same."

Macario then related this idea to another case of equivalence we had recently discussed. He explained, "The answer to the fraction never changes, like when you add $5 + 2 = 7$ and $2 + 5 = 7$. The answer never changes, only the numbers." 220

Rabia said, "When you take a fraction and double the numerator and denominator, it gets smaller, because you split the pieces in half." But when pressed, she said that the fraction didn't get smaller, but the pieces 225 were smaller.

Ida picked up on Rabia's idea and drew a picture to illustrate.

$\frac{1}{3}$		$\frac{1}{3}$		$\frac{1}{3}$	
$\frac{1}{6}$	$\frac{1}{6}$	$\frac{1}{6}$	$\frac{1}{6}$	$\frac{1}{6}$	$\frac{1}{6}$

She showed that when the denominator increased from 3 to 6, the pieces got smaller. But if you take two of them, you have the same amount as $\frac{1}{3}$. 230

C A S E   20

Today's number is 1

Zura
GRADE 4, MARCH

I asked seven students to join me in a small group with their papers showing their ideas for how to make 1 using only fractions (e.g., $\frac{3}{4} + \frac{1}{4}$, $\frac{1}{2} + \frac{1}{2}$). I wanted to see how these students were making sense of numbers like $\frac{4}{4}$. I wondered if they would be able to talk about why, when the numerator and denominator were the same number, the number is 235 always equal to 1.

TEACHER: I noticed that many of you were making equivalent fractions for this task.

I wrote down the numbers suggested by the students:

$$\frac{8192}{8192} \qquad \frac{9186}{9186} \qquad \frac{4}{4} \qquad \frac{8}{8} \qquad \frac{16{,}224}{16{,}224} \qquad \frac{16}{16}$$

240

TEACHER: What patterns do you notice?

IRIS: I notice that the top and bottom numbers are the same.

BETSY: You mean, the numerator and denominator.

IRIS: Yeah, that's what I mean.

TEACHER: Can someone tell me why this works? Why, when you have the same number for the numerator and the denominator, does it equal 1?

245

BETSY: Oh, I know! 16 pieces are in the whole, and you have 16 pieces. That equals one whole.

The other students nodded and said they agreed with Betsy.

250

TEACHER: Will this always work? When you have the same number for the numerator and the denominator, will it always equal 1?

KURT: Not with negative numbers.

IRIS: Not with prime numbers or 13. You can't divide 13 in half.

255

ANDY: You don't have to divide 13 in half. You can have a fraction that equals $\frac{13}{13}$.

IRIS: Oh.

TEACHER: What were you thinking about, Iris? Why won't 13 work?

IRIS: I think it will work now. Wait, does the shape always have to be a rectangle or a square?

260

TEACHER: What do you mean by that?

IRIS: Can you come back to me?

I appreciated Iris's honesty and her willingness to take some time to listen and think about what she had just said.

265

LOUIS: It won't work on *all* numbers, but on all the numbers I tried, it worked. I kept doubling my numbers, and it worked.

Zura

LILI: It works all the time. If you break up a shape into an equal
number of pieces, you can put them back together, as long as
they are the same number of pieces—like puzzle pieces that
you put back together. The denominator is like the number
of pieces in the whole puzzle, and the numerator is the
number of puzzle pieces in the fraction.

BETSY: It will always work if you have the numerator and denominator as the same number. It will always equal one whole,
like 16 pieces in the whole square; $\frac{16}{16} = 1$. I think . . . it's
really hard to say in words.

ANDY: It will always work. If you have 16 puzzle pieces and
16 spaces, it would always work. I'm having trouble
saying what I mean. I understand it in my head.

CONOR: Yeah, I could prove it to my brother, but not right now.

LUCAS: I know what to say, but I can't remember . . . what is a
numerator and a denominator again?

We stopped to review the definitions of numerator and denominator, and
then returned to the generalization on the table.

LILI: It will always work! I know it will always work! But maybe
not with negative numbers, but most people don't work
with negative numbers. Is there such a thing as negative
fractions?

Lili looked around the table. No one had an answer for her, but
everyone seemed to agree that this was a puzzling question.

I chose not to answer Lili's question, either. For now, I wanted
students to work with images of fractions in terms of a whole divided
into parts—parts they can count with whole numbers. If Lili felt
solid with those ideas and was ready to think about negative
fractions, she now had a question that would be useful for her to
mull over.

As I review this discussion, I see that Iris has some misconceptions
to work through. I'll need to give her more experiences that allow her to
think about a variety of fractions. I'll also need to pay more attention to
where Conor and Lucas are.

But from their comments, it seems that Lili, Betsy, and Andy were
holding onto the meanings of numerator and denominator, together with

an image of what fractions are. Lili's image of a jigsaw puzzle—thinking
of the number of pieces in the whole puzzle as the denominator and some
number of those pieces as the numerator—helps to make the general
claim. Lili states adamantly, "It will always work!"

But then Lili reconsiders. She seems to be aware that the puzzle image
implies numerators and denominators greater than 0. She knows the
puzzle doesn't help her think about fractions in which the numerator or
denominator might take on negative values.

Although Lili doesn't mention it, the puzzle image does not help one
think about $\frac{0}{0}$, either. In fact, that is the exception to the rule the students
are considering. At some future time, they will learn that $\frac{a}{a} = 1$ for all
values of a not equal to 0.

I am interested in Louis's comment, that it won't work on *all* numbers,
but on all the numbers he tried, it worked. He recognizes that it's not
enough to test a general claim on specific cases to conclude that the
claim is true over an infinite set. But if he returns to the meaning of the
numerator and denominator, will he be able to see a general claim for
the numbers we are considering here in fourth grade? That is, implicit
in our work on fractions, denominators are always greater than or equal
to 1; numerators are always greater than or equal to 0. And within these
constraints, whenever the numerator and denominator are equal, the
fraction is equal to 1.

C A S E   21

Fraction flags

Kate

"Fraction Flags" is set of activities used in *Parts of a Whole, Parts of a
Group*, the second-grade fractions unit from the *Investigations in Number,
Data*, and *Space* (2nd. ed., Pearson Learning, 2008). In these activities,
flags are used as a context for looking at both unit fractions $\left(\frac{1}{2}, \frac{1}{3}, \frac{1}{4}\right)$ and
non-unit fractions $\left(\frac{2}{3}, \frac{3}{4}\right)$.

Kate

GRADE 2, MARCH

Prior to the lesson described here, the students had worked with the unit fractions. They had colored in and labeled flags that were divided into two, three, or four parts, coloring each section of a flag a different color. For example, for a flag that was divided into thirds, a student might color one section red, one blue, and one green, and label them $\frac{1}{3}$ red, $\frac{1}{3}$ blue, and $\frac{1}{3}$ green.

335

In this activity, the students use the same context to explore flags that have more than one part the same color. We began by referring to a chart we had made that showed a flag divided into different numbers of parts. For each flag, the chart showed how many parts, and what each part was called in both words and numbers (for example, half and $\frac{1}{2}$).

340

We reviewed what each unit fraction was called. Then I showed them the flag of Nigeria, which is divided into vertical thirds: the first and the last third are green, and the middle third is white.

We talked through what each of the parts is called, and I explained that since two of the thirds are green, we say that two-thirds are green, and we write it as $\frac{2}{3}$.

345

When we looked at the flag of Colombia, which is divided into horizontal quarters, the discussion quickly moved into the territory of equivalent fractions. The top half is yellow, the next quarter down is blue, and the bottom quarter is red. I asked who could tell me how many parts were in the flag. I called on Keegan.

350

KEEGAN: Four.

TEACHER: There are 4 parts. How much of the flag is red? Colin?

Making Meaning for Operations

Kate

GRADE 2, MARCH

COLIN:	A quarter?
TEACHER:	OK, one quarter. [*I wrote: $\frac{1}{4}$ is red.*] How much is blue? Holly?
HOLLY:	One quarter.
TEACHER:	[*writing*] One quarter is blue. And how much of the flag is yellow? Sadie?
SADIE:	Two quarters.
TEACHER:	[*writing*] Two quarters are yellow.
JOSHUA:	[*speaking with certainty*] That means a half.
TEACHER:	That means a half? How do you know?
JOSHUA:	Because two quarters have already gone by [*referring to the red and the blue having gone by in our discussion*], so another two quarters would be another half. But if they're both yellow, then both yellow ones combined together would be a half. So since there's two yellow spots, it would be a half.

Reed looked eager to speak, so I asked if he wanted to add something.

REED:	What he is trying to say is that two quarters makes one half, because one quarter is this big and another is this big, so that makes it a half. And two halves, because there's two over here [*points to the red and blue*] and then two over here [*points to the yellow*], and they're both the same.
JOSHUA:	But the bottom half is red and blue, so that makes both of them a quarter. But the top is all yellow, so that makes it a whole half.
REED:	Because the top is kind of, since it's all one color, that makes it half is one color, and then a quarter is blue and a quarter is red. But if you put them together and pretend they were all blue or all red, it would show that the two bottom ones were a half and the top ones were a half.
TEACHER:	So, can someone else say what Reed just said?
KEEGAN:	I think what Reed is saying is if there's two quarters out of four, it's basically half.

355

360

365

370

375

380

385

Kate

TEACHER:	And do you remember why he said it was basically half? How he kind of proved it?
KEEGAN:	It's like the same length as each other. The bottom ones are just the same as this [*points to the yellow*], so it's half.
REED:	It's more like a line of symmetry.
TEACHER:	So come up and tell us which is the line of symmetry, Reed.
REED:	Here's where it splits in half [*he points to the line between the yellow and blue sections*]. And this is the line of symmetry between the quarters [*points to the line between the red and blue sections*], and if you color over that, the line of symmetry is the line between the halves.
TEACHER:	You're saying it's like there's a line here that makes it a quarter, and if you color over that line, then that line is invisible and then it's a half. And Tracy is shaking her head yes. You agree with him Tracy? [*She nods.*] Colin, you've been dying to talk. What did you want to say?
COLIN:	Since it's like red is 25¢, blue is 50¢, one yellow is 75¢ and one more is a dollar.
TEACHER:	You're thinking about it as money! That's really cool. If you're thinking about it as money, then this would be 25¢ [*points to a quarter of the flag*] and this would be 25¢ [*points to another quarter*]. This would be 75¢ [*indicating three quarters of the flag*], and this [*the whole flag*] would be a dollar.
COLIN:	Once you add a quarter to another quarter, it keeps getting bigger and bigger and bigger.
TEACHER:	Ah. Colin is saying something a little different.
JOSHUA:	Do you mean a money quarter or do you mean a quarter of the rectangle?
TEACHER:	Hold on. Colin is saying that when you add a quarter to another quarter, it gets bigger and bigger.
REED:	Oh, because why it got bigger is because there's a bunch of quarters which makes the halves.

390

395

400

405

410

415

Kate

TEACHER:	It makes two halves? Oh, all these quarters together make two halves?
REED:	Yeah.
JOSHUA:	You can make them into two . . .

Now all three boys were talking at once, trying to explain what they meant. I wanted the class to be able to sort this out and see the connection Colin was making between the fraction flags and a context that he knew really well, money, so I tried to slow the conversation down. Reed continued.

REED:	He's thinking of two halves. Two halves make one dollar.
TEACHER:	He's thinking about the quarter being like the quarter we have . . .
COLIN:	I split it like right in the middle line, and then I had two, four. And then I think of money, I think of 25¢. Like one whole thing is 25¢, then 50¢.
TEACHER:	So you're thinking like it's a quarter of a dollar. Joshua, you asked if it meant a quarter of this [*pointing to the rectangle cut into quarters*] or a quarter of a dollar. One of the reasons we call a quarter of a dollar a *quarter* is because it takes four of them to make a dollar. So when we have four quarters, then we have a dollar. Each one is a quarter of a dollar.
JOSHUA:	And when you split things into four different parts, then it's quarters.
TEACHER:	We took the money in a dollar and split it into four parts.
JOSHUA:	So then there would be four quarters.
TEACHER:	So then there would be four quarters.
JOSHUA:	And that's why they call it a quarter.
TEACHER:	Exactly, Joshua.

We talked a little bit more while other children worked to make sense of this idea that a quarter (25¢) was really one-fourth of a dollar. I can see that this is really confusing. It's the same word, and it means the same

in reference to a dollar, but it is something of its own as well: an object   450
whose name is "a quarter."

Sadie then drew our attention back to the flag of Nigeria. She said you
could cut the flag in half, and then you'd have a third and part of a third.
Reed said that if you drew a line down the middle of the green part, it
makes a fourth. So I drew this out for the class and asked if the new parts   455
were all quarters.

The class responded with a resounding no. Sadie said that each part
would be a sixth. She pointed to each section as she counted: 1 [*the first
small green section*], 2 [*the second small green section*], 3, 4 [*the white section*],
5, 6 [*the last green section*]. She concluded, "Each one is a sixth."   460

TEACHER: Do you want me to split up the others?

CLOE: It's not even if you don't split up the other ones.

Cloe and Sadie talked a bit more, and I asked someone to restate what
they were saying.

CLARA: If they aren't all the same size, then they aren't all the same.   465

TEACHER: That's what we were saying the other day, that they have to
be equal pieces, right?

We finished the conversation with some other observations, and the
children went on to the paper part of the activity, filling in their new set
of flags.   470

I am left thinking again about this sense of sameness or "equalness"
that they are bringing to their fraction work and how those images will
serve them as they move on to harder fraction work in future years. In
fact, I wonder how all of these images will serve them, including Colin's
image of fractions being connected to money.   475

C H A P T E R

5

Combining shares, or adding fractions

CASE 22	Sharing brownies or adding fractions	Mary Ann, Grade 4, February
CASE 23	How many ways can you add 1/3 to 1/4? Or, interesting stuff happens!	Henry, Grade 6, December
CASE 24	"Doling out" and fractions	Greta, Grades 6–7, November

Earlier, in chapter 1, you read cases describing students' work in whole-number addition and subtraction. In this chapter, we return to addition, but now we examine students who are working on adding fractions. What do we learn about the meaning of addition when we explore the complexities of adding fractions? What must we understand about fractions in order to figure out how to add them?

Sharing brownies or adding fractions

MaryAnn
GRADE 4, FEBRUARY

When my colleague, Janie, gave me her Problem of the Week last week, I
felt that it would fit right in with what my class was doing with fractions.
Each week, Janie picks a problem and distributes it to all the staff at
our school—teachers, administrators, support staff, everyone. And lots
of people work on it. Our staff development coordinator has declared   5
herself "math phobic," but she works on the problem every week and is
determined to learn how to solve problems like these. The custodian also
submits his solution each week. Some of the teachers give the problems to
their students.

Anyway, this particular problem came from *Seeing Fractions: A Unit for*   10
the Upper Elementary Grades (California Department of Education, 1990;
developed by TERC). It reads as follows:

 I invited 8 people to my party (including me) and I only had
3 brownies. How much did each person get if they had fair
shares?   15

We were still hungry, and I finally found 2 more brownies in
the bottom of the cookie jar. They were stale, but we ate them
anyway. This time, how much did each person get?

How much brownie in all did each person eat?
20
The problem is quite a bit more complex than those we had been
working on. It has three parts, and the third question involves adding
fractions with unlike denominators. We hadn't yet done anything like
that. I don't think I would have chosen this problem on my own, but
since it arrived in my mailbox, I decided to give it a try. I wondered what
my students would do with it.   25

MaryAnn
GRADE 4, FEBRUARY

We have spent three days of math class on the problem. The children worked on their own or in pairs, as they chose, while I moved around the room holding discussions to see how they understood the problem. Sometimes, I asked the children to share their strategies with the rest of the class. Now, on this third day, I'm looking over their written work. 30

Although everybody wrote something that related to fractions, a couple of children didn't pick up on the concept of *fair shares*. They took the 3 brownies, broke them into 8 pieces, and wrote out $\frac{1}{2} + \frac{1}{2} + \frac{1}{2} + \frac{1}{2} + \frac{1}{4} + \frac{1}{4} + \frac{1}{4} + \frac{1}{4}$. They felt satisfied that this was a solution 35 to the problem.

Most of the children did come up with a valid answer to each of the three questions. I am quite interested in Maribel's work. She has devised a procedure that she applies to all cases of fair shares: Cut the brownies so that each person gets one piece from each brownie. For example, 40 to answer the first question, she drew 8 faces for the 8 people at the party and drew 3 brownies, which she cut into eighths. She then began distributing the pieces to the people. Each time she distributed 8 pieces, she crossed out the brownie they came from. After she finished distributing the pieces, she counted them up. "They each get $\frac{3}{8}$," 45 she wrote. Maribel then applied the same procedure to answer the second question, concluding, "They each get $\frac{2}{8}$."

Looking at Maribel's work on the first two questions (see Figure 5.1), I would have expected her to say something like, "If they first got $\frac{3}{8}$ and then later got $\frac{2}{8}$, that means that they got $\frac{5}{8}$ all together." 50 But that's not what she did. Instead, she treated the third question as if it were a completely new problem: 8 people shared 5 brownies. She drew her 8 faces and drew her 5 brownies and applied the same procedure again (see Figure 5.2). There's certainly nothing incorrect about her procedure, and she felt satisfied with her answer of $\frac{5}{8}$. 55 I wonder if she recognizes that she could have solved the problem by adding.

Figure 5.1 Maribel's work on the first two parts of the brownie-sharing problem

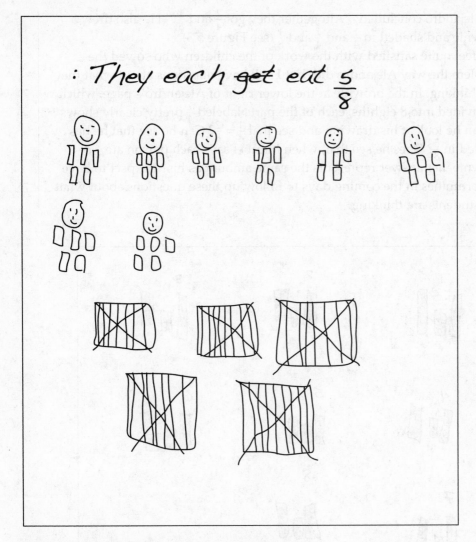

Figure 5.2 Maribel's work on the third question in the brownie problem

Alejandro used a method common to several other students in the
class. He first saw that 2 brownies could be distributed among 8 people
if you cut them into fourths, and he drew out the 8 quarter-portions.
The third brownie could be cut into eighths, so for each person he drew
an eighth next to the fourth. He concluded, "First they got $\frac{1}{4}$ and $\frac{1}{8}$." For
the second part of the problem, he again distributed the 2 brownies by
cutting them into fourths, drawing in another quarter-portion for each
person: "Then they got $\frac{1}{4}$." Looking at his pictorial representation,

60

65

Alejandro concluded, "Altogether they got $\frac{2}{4}$ and $\frac{1}{8}$." He also drew a brownie and shaded in $\frac{1}{4}$ and $\frac{1}{4}$ and $\frac{1}{8}$ (see Figure 5.3).

I feel quite satisfied with the work of the children who solved the problem the way Alejandro did, but I still have questions about what they are thinking. In the brownie at the lower right of Alejandro's page, which he divided into 8 eighths, each of the parts labeled $\frac{1}{4}$ pretty clearly shows $\frac{2}{8}$. Can he look at his drawing and see that $\frac{1}{4} = \frac{2}{8}$? Can he see that he has shaded in $\frac{5}{8}$? Does he see that, when Maribel says each person ate $\frac{5}{8}$ of a brownie, her answer represents the same amount as his? I expect to have opportunities in the coming days to follow up these questions about what my students are thinking.

70

75

Figure 5.3 Alejandro's work on the brownie-sharing problem

MaryAnn

Usually I distribute my time pretty evenly among my students, asking them questions while they are working. Sometimes, however, I give more of my time to children who especially need attention; then I catch up with the others later. During the three days that we worked on this problem, I spent much of my time with Jackson.

Jackson is a sweet kid who is almost always disorganized. At the beginning of the school year, I found it hard to listen to him; he always seemed to be rambling, and it was difficult to make sense of what he was saying. His classmates seemed to have the same reaction. However, in recent years I have learned to listen hard for the ideas my students are trying to express, and when I persevered, I found that listening to Jackson offered unexpected rewards. He has good mathematical insights. And when I listen hard and take seriously what Jackson is saying, so do his classmates. Their relationship to him has improved since September.

On the day that I handed out the problem, I moved through the classroom, looking over children's shoulders, pausing to listen to their conversations, sometimes asking them questions so that I could better understand what they were thinking. By the time I got to Jackson, he had answers for all three questions. However, his page was so messy, I couldn't interpret what he had done (see Figure 5.4). When I asked him to explain, he could share some confident and correct thinking. Yet, as he tried to retrace what he had done, he lost track of his thinking and couldn't make sense of his own disorganized written work.

For the first question, Jackson was able to explain quickly that 3 brownies had been cut up so that 8 people each received $\frac{1}{4}$ from the first two brownies and then each received $\frac{1}{8}$ from the third. He noted that each fair share was $\frac{1}{4} + \frac{1}{8}$. (Unlike Alejandro, Jackson used the plus sign instead of the word *and*.)

Jackson's illustration for the second question showed 2 brownies cut into 8 equal shares of $\frac{1}{4}$ each. His answer to the second question was $\frac{1}{4}$.

The third part got very messy. Unfortunately for Jackson, much good thinking gets lost because of his poor organizational skills. It was difficult for him to figure out what he had done in this section. He knew what the question was, but he seemed to feel that he had to reconstruct the whole problem before he could reach a conclusion. (This is what Maribel had done, too.) I wonder why he didn't realize that he had already figured out much of what he needed to know, and that he just needed to use the information from the first two parts.

When Jackson worked to distribute 5 brownies among 8 people, he   115
figured that they got $\frac{1}{4}$ and $\frac{1}{4}$ and $\frac{1}{8}$. We can see on his paper that he
wrote $\frac{1}{4} + \frac{1}{4} + \frac{1}{8}$ in a vertical column and came up with an answer of $\frac{3}{8}$.

At this point, it appeared that Jackson had separated the numbers
from the problem context. When I asked him how he got $\frac{3}{8}$, he explained
that he added the 1s (the numerators) and then added $4 + 4$, two of the   120
denominators, to get 8. He decided that since the other denominator is
also 8, it stays the same, "So $\frac{3}{8}$." Jackson wanted to be satisfied with this
answer and wanted me to leave him alone. Instead, I asked him to think
about the third part of the problem and told him we'd talk about it again
later. This was the end of the first day.   125

Figure 5.4 Jackson's seat work on the brownie questions, Day 1

Figure 5.5 Jackson's board work explaining his solution to the brownie problem, Day 2

The next day I had some of the children share their solutions on the board. Jackson came to the board to talk about the third question (see Figure 5.5).

JACKSON: All right, draw 5 brownies, like this. [*He draws 5 squares.*] Cut the first two into 4 parts each [*which he does*], and then make the next one into 8 parts. [*Without speaking, he also divides the last two squares into eighths.*]   130

Although I knew that this would work out OK, I wondered aloud why he had changed his strategy from yesterday's attempt. He shrugged. Then he counted up what each person got and came up with an answer   135 of $\frac{1}{4}$ and $\frac{3}{8}$. This time he didn't try to combine them to create a single fractional number.

I was struck by the clarity of Jackson's presentation. Although he frequently loses focus when working with complex problems, once focused, he can confidently arrive at an accurate solution.   140

However, our work on the problem—and my thinking about Jackson—wasn't done. The next day, we continued the group discussion about the children's various solutions. When one child said that he didn't understand what Jackson had done, Jackson offered to explain it again, one-on-one. I was interested to hear how he would rephrase the problem   145 and his solution, so I listened in.

MaryAnn

Figure 5.6 Jackson's attempt to explain his solution to a classmate, Day 3

Jackson showed how the first 3 brownies could be distributed among 8 people to make portions of $\frac{1}{4} + \frac{1}{8}$ (see Figure 5.6). He then showed how the next 2 brownies would give each person $\frac{1}{4}$. I noted that he had gone back to his original strategy. And then, in a change from his

Making Meaning for Operations

first-day approach, Jackson began to work on the third question without redoing the entire problem; he seemed to realize that the answer could be derived from the first two parts. However, he did come up with the same answer: $\frac{1}{4} + \frac{1}{4} + \frac{1}{8} = \frac{3}{8}$. I wanted to hear more.

TEACHER: I see that you did some work with the fractions over here. [*I point to some crossed-out figures on his paper.*] I'm wondering why you crossed out some numbers.

JACKSON: I was adding the 1 + 1 + 1 and it came to 3, but then I went to add the bottoms [4 + 4 + 8] and it didn't make sense. There's nothing here that's 16, and the numbers I was getting wouldn't match the brownies. When I looked at the brownies, I could see that each person had $\frac{1}{4}$ and $\frac{1}{4}$ and $\frac{1}{8}$, and I know the $\frac{1}{4}$ and $\frac{1}{4}$ make $\frac{1}{2}$, and then $\frac{1}{8}$. So, I'm telling you each person had a share of $\frac{1}{2}$ and $\frac{1}{8}$.

It turns out that when Jackson tried to add, he wasn't simply looking at the numerals without considering the problem context. After all, he rejected $\frac{3}{16}$ as an answer—it didn't make sense in this context. So he manipulated the symbols in a different way and came up with an answer, $\frac{3}{8}$, that seemed more reasonable to him.

Jackson had come up with three different correct representations for a single fair share in this problem:

$$\frac{1}{4} + \frac{1}{4} + \frac{1}{8} \qquad \frac{1}{4} \text{ and } \frac{3}{8} \qquad \frac{1}{2} \text{ and } \frac{1}{8}$$

I wonder how he perceives Alejandro's $\frac{2}{4}$ and $\frac{1}{8}$, or Maribel's answer of $\frac{5}{8}$.

Up ahead for all my students is the work of sorting out the ideas behind adding fractions with unlike denominators. I'll be watching how they think this through, building on the ideas they already have in place.

CASE 23

How many ways can you add 1/3 to 1/4? Or, interesting stuff happens!

Henry

GRADE 6, DECEMBER

This year I teach sixth-grade math to three different groups each day. I have found that the more control I assume and structure I apply, the more similar the three classes will be on a given day. When I give up some of that control and allow the students to determine more of the agenda, those groups move in wildly divergent directions.

A recent lesson looked quite simple in my plan book. We had been adding fractions with like denominators and had begun to get ready to deal with unlike denominators. We had experimented with finding common multiples, explored equivalency, practiced simplifying fractions, and begun changing fractions to higher terms.

I was feeling that we were in the thick of a computational jungle, and I wanted us to look at some concepts together. I also wanted to get an idea of what my students were thinking. For my lesson, I asked the students to make pictures (diagrams) of what is happening when we add $\frac{1}{3}$ to $\frac{1}{4}$. Each class handled it very differently.

In the first class, I started out by asking the group to draw what happens when we add $\frac{1}{3}$ to $\frac{1}{3}$. Alexandra came to the board to show us her picture. She drew it out this way:

first $\frac{1}{3}$	first $\frac{1}{3}$	
$\frac{1}{3}$	$\frac{1}{3}$	

This seemed quite straightforward; no one offered a different notion or any objections. Thinking that this was just how I saw it, I plowed forward

180

185

190

195

with the main lesson, asking the class to work in groups to draw a picture of $\frac{1}{3} + \frac{1}{4}$. (There were a few other instructions, too, such as create a story problem to accompany the numbers, and explain your group's picture and approach to another group, but for this case I am focusing on the pictures they drew.)

200

All groups used Alexandra's work as a model, and although there were certainly some moments of struggle, groups produced this type of drawing:

$$\frac{1}{3} + \frac{1}{4} = \frac{7}{12}$$

When asked how exactly they came up with the twelfths, they answered that they "found a common denominator and changed to higher terms" and so on. In other words, they mimicked the computation we had been doing in the previous days and did not look beneath the computational surface of the problem. It wasn't really their fault either, for this is sort of what I expected, what I wanted. This was an obvious reaction to what I had set up.

205

210

The second class began with the same instructions; however, our model student, Ramón, opened up a mathematical Pandora's Box with his drawing of $\frac{1}{3} + \frac{1}{3}$:

He explained this to be equal to $\frac{2}{3}$, but Tanya wondered, "Isn't that really equal to 2 out of 6 or $\frac{2}{6}$, which is just $\frac{1}{3}$? But how could $\frac{1}{3} + \frac{1}{3} = \frac{1}{3}$?"

215

In trying to sort this out, Colin came up with this example:

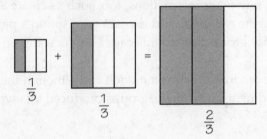

Of course the different-sized wholes then brought up other issues. Ten minutes into this lesson I had discovered that a good deal of confusion lived just beneath the surface—not the computational surface, but the conceptual one. I know that it was there in the first class, too, but I just wasn't able to get it to bubble up.

For the third class, I completely abandoned my preconceived plans and expectations. I decided to do away with the model example of $\frac{1}{3} + \frac{1}{3}$ and to start with $\frac{1}{3} + \frac{1}{4}$. I asked the students to try not to think about any computational angles, but to attempt to picture their understandings. This approach yielded entirely different results. Lizette showed this diagram to get started on $\frac{1}{3} + \frac{1}{4}$:

3 rows by 4 columns = twelfths

We began to investigate if this type of picture would be a good way to come up with a lowest common multiple for two numbers. The conversations and investigations were lively. In the midst of it all, some kids were doing exactly what I do when I am involved in similar situations as a student. They were "doing their own thing," going off on tangents, discovering ideas that have been experienced by others millions of times but that were new to them. Why didn't this environment exist in the other two classes? I wondered and still wonder. I'm sure that much of the answer is that I did not allow it to exist, or, to put it more mildly, I did not effectively sponsor it.

Henry
GRADE 6, DECEMBER

As this class ended, one student, Ming-hua, came up to tell me that he had discovered something cool: 240

$$\frac{1}{3}$$
$$+\frac{1}{4}$$
$$\frac{7}{12} \quad \text{because it's } \frac{3+4}{3\times4}$$

$$\frac{1}{15}$$
$$+\frac{1}{2}$$
$$\frac{17}{30} \quad \text{because it's } \frac{15+2}{15\times2}$$

My reaction to Ming-hua? "WOW!"

In conclusion, what does it all mean? Honestly, I'm not sure. I know that does not establish closure, so . . . I guess it means that the teacher sets the tone for the lesson and the environment of the class—consciously, but often times unconsciously, too. When I don't expect my students to be clones of me and merely follow my lead, when I genuinely listen to their questions and don't rush to answer them, interesting stuff happens. 245

C A S E   24

"Doling out" and fractions

Greta
GRADES 6 AND 7 (SPECIAL ED), NOVEMBER

I have been thinking about how my students use "doling" as a strategy for solving fraction problems of this type: division of whole numbers with the remainder expressed as a fraction. The strategy of doling out has its pros and cons. On the upside, doling is very systematic and easy to understand. On the downside, some of my students can't reassemble all the fractional pieces into just one fraction. For others the equivalency issue is akin to changing the problem. 250 255

For example, consider one boy's approach to this problem:

> **?** 4 kids share 19 pizzas. How much will each kid get?

Gunther will dole out all the wholes first: The 4 kids each get 4 whole pizzas. Then taking the 3 remaining pizzas, he will cut 2 of them in half,

Chapter 5 111

dole out each $\frac{1}{2}$, then cut the last pizza in 4 pieces and dole out $\frac{1}{4}$ to each 260
kid. Gunther writes as his answer: "The first boy gets 4 wholes and a
half and $\frac{1}{4}$. The second boy gets 4 wholes and a half and $\frac{1}{4}$. The third boy
gets . . . ." Gunther is very systematic in breaking down the pizza into
ever smaller pieces. But when Mercedes says that her answer, $4\frac{3}{4}$, is the
same as his, he initially objects. She shows him how his half pieces can be 265
cut into fourths. "But I know I got the answer; this changes my drawing,"
he protests. There are two underlying issues for him, I think: He doesn't
yet know that mixed numbers are conventionally expressed as a whole
and one fraction, and that fractional pieces like $\frac{1}{2}$ and $\frac{1}{4}$ can be added.

Another boy handled the following problem in an interesting way: 270

? 3 kids share one stick of gum. How much does each get?

Dominic wrote:

$\frac{4}{4}$ equals 1 whole. So we divide it into four parts: $\frac{1}{4}$ $\frac{2}{4}$ $\frac{3}{4}$ $\frac{4}{4}$. Each kid is
going to get $\frac{1}{4}$. So $\frac{3}{4}$ are gone. [There] is $\frac{1}{4}$ left so we need to divide $\frac{1}{4}$
into $\frac{1}{12}$ pieces. [Each kid gets] $\frac{1}{4}$ and $\frac{1}{12}$. 275

Dominic's drawing looked first as shown at left; then he extended the
three horizontal lines to make twelfths.

While showing and describing his work, Dominic realized that $\frac{1}{4}$ and
$\frac{1}{12}$ could also be called $\frac{4}{12}$. When I asked if there was an easier way to do
this problem, Dominic returned with a drawing showing thirds: 280

Dominic's work is shown in Figure 5.7.

Greta

Dominic, like Gunther, would have left his answer as $\frac{1}{4} + \frac{1}{12}$, except that our conversation about his drawing led him to the other answer. Again I started thinking about how students sometimes shy away from combining fractional pieces on the initial solution.

285

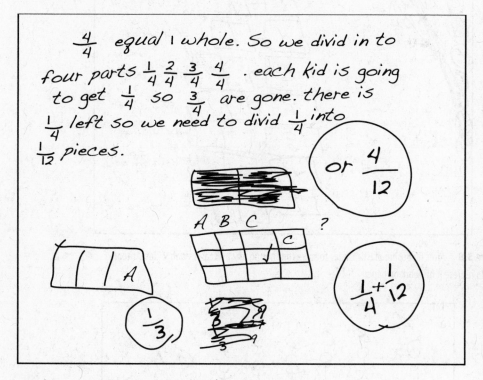

Figure 5.7   Dominic's work showing how 3 kids share 1 stick of gum

In another problem of this type, 9 kids shared 21 pizzas. How much did each get? For this problem, some students chose to use small plastic circles to represent the pizzas. Antonio was able to dole out 2 wholes for each of the 9 kids. Then on the "leftover" 3 circles, he drew lines on the plastic and numbered 9 slices. When asked about his work, Antonio explained that each kid got 2 wholes and $\frac{1}{9}$ and $\frac{1}{9}$ and $\frac{1}{9}$. However, while he worked on recording his ideas on paper (see Figure 5.8), he forgot how many ninths each kid got and gave 2 and $\frac{1}{9}$ as his answer.

290

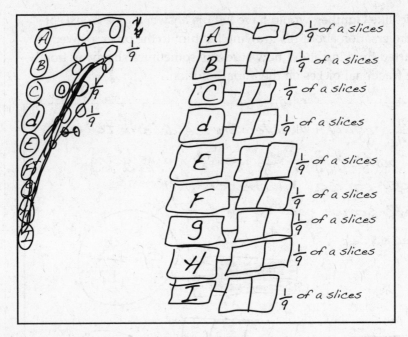

Figure 5.8 After first using plastic circles to solve the sharing of 21 pizzas among 9 kids, Antonio tried to represent his work on paper

Figure 5.9 In Zoe's work, showing her solution to 9 kids sharing 21 pizzas, she doles out 18 pizzas first and divides the leftover 3 into thirds

On the same problem Zoe showed an impressive ability to keep straight in her head a lot of information. She laid out 36 plastic circles in a 9-by-4 array. I thought that she was totally confused. She proved me wrong. She told me the first row across was the 9 kids. The next 2 rows were the wholes. The bottom row was the thirds. I was amazed since all the circles were identical. When she worked on paper (as shown in Figure 5.9), Zoe represented the kids, whole pizzas, and thirds differently. That was less confusing for me.

295

300

C H A P T E R

6

Taking portions of portions, or multiplying fractions

CASE 25	Clock faces and equivalence	Ann, Grade 6, November
CASE 26	Multiplication of mixed numbers	Sarita, Grade 6, November
CASE 27	What I want my students to understand about multiplication	Henry, Grade 6, December

In chapter 2, you read cases describing students' work in whole-number multiplication and division. In this chapter, we examine students who are working on multiplying fractions. What sorts of situations could be modeled by, say, $\frac{1}{3} \times \frac{1}{4}$, and what is it about such situations that make multiplication appropriate? What representations are especially useful for depicting multiplication of fractions?

Clock faces and equivalence

Ann

As my sixth-grade students explored equivalent fractions, I used a lesson from TERC's *Investigations*, in the *What's That Portion* unit. It asked the students to look at clock faces and determine what portion of the clock face the hour hand has passed through since 12 o'clock (see Figure 6.1). I have come to expect the unexpected when conducting a math lesson, and this lesson was no exception.

Jaclyn started with the clock reading 1 o'clock. "I think it's $\frac{1}{12}$ because there are 12 parts and 1 of them is being used."

Rusty chimed in, "It could be a $\frac{5}{60}$, too, because there are 60 minutes in an hour and 5 minutes are the portion shown."

Midori suggested, "It could be $\frac{2}{24}$ because that is equal to $\frac{1}{12}$."

"What portion would $\frac{1}{24}$ represent on the clock?" I asked.

Liam raised his hand. "It would be $2\frac{1}{2}$ minutes, because $\frac{2}{24}$ is 5 minutes, so half of 5 minutes is $2\frac{1}{2}$ minutes."

I asked if there were any other ideas, and Amini spoke up: "It could also be $\frac{1}{3}$ of $\frac{1}{4}$ of the clock face."

This response initially brought puzzled looks and questions to the other students and to me. What was Amini seeing? First he was looking at the whole clock face and breaking it into quarters; then looking at just the one quarter, he noticed that a third of it was the portion marked. This ability to look at a portion of a portion was unexpected.

As we looked at the other clock faces, students continued to point out this portion-of-a-portion equivalency. Ferris said that the clock face showing 2 o'clock was $\frac{2}{3}$ of $\frac{1}{4}$. For 3 o'clock, Liam said the portion shown was $\frac{1}{6}$ plus $\frac{1}{2}$ of $\frac{1}{6}$. Ferris suggested that we could also call it $\frac{1}{2}$ of $\frac{1}{2}$. Midori saw 4 o'clock as $\frac{4}{6}$ of $\frac{1}{2}$. Similar examples happened on each clock face.

Not all students were able to see these equivalencies. What is necessary for a student—or a teacher—to see them? I speculate that one must be able to identify the whole first. In this case, the clock face was the whole. After recognizing this, you have to notice a portion of the whole,

Figure 6.1   Clock Fractions from grade 5, unit 4, *What's That Portion?* in TERC's *Investigations in Number, Data, and Space* (2008), Pearson Education

such as $\frac{1}{2}$ or $\frac{1}{4}$, and have *this* become the "whole" you focus on for a while—but you still need to hold onto its relationship with the whole clock face. You then compare the new whole ($\frac{1}{2}$ or $\frac{1}{4}$, for example) to the portion indicated by the hour hand. Is the hour hand's movement a sixth of the new portion, a half of it, a third of it? To do this, someone must be able to see relationships within relationships. I feel that this is a big mathematical issue for my students.

35

Multiplication of mixed numbers

Sarita

I asked the students in my sixth-grade class to solve the following
problem by drawing a large, clearly labeled picture:

?   What is the area of a rectangle that has a width of $2\frac{3}{4}$ units
and a length of $3\frac{2}{3}$ units?   40

As I was walking around the classroom, listening to and observing
students working on the problem, I overheard the following comment:

YURI: Usually all you have to do to find the area is to multiply the
length times the width, but because we have fractions, you   45
can't do that.

We had spent many weeks working on area and perimeter problems,
so the students were familiar with finding the area of a region by
counting the number of units or, in the case of rectangles, by multiplying
the width times the length. Why did Yuri think this method would not   50
apply with fractions?

When we started the whole-group discussion, Olivia volunteered to
come to the board and discuss her strategy for solving the problem. She
carefully drew her picture on the board.

$3\frac{2}{3}$

$2\frac{3}{4}$

| OLIVIA: | You can get some of the area but not all of it. | 55 |

TEACHER: What part of the area can you get?

OLIVIA: I know that the length times the width is the area, so
$2 \times 3 = 6$.

TEACHER: Where is the 2×3, or the 6, in the picture?

OLIVIA: The big squares are the wholes and you can just count 6.   60
The smaller pieces you can count, too, but they don't count
as wholes.

TEACHER: Why not?

OLIVIA: Those pieces aren't whole squares the way that the other
ones are, because of the fractions. So [*counting to herself*],   65
there are 4 of those [*she points to the rectangles at the top right*],
and that is $1\frac{1}{3}$. If you put 4 fourths together, that's 2 wholes
and $\frac{1}{4}$ left. But I don't know how to count the other pieces.

TEACHER: Why not?

OLIVIA: They are like pieces of pieces of something.   70

KYLE: Like fractions of pieces when the pieces are fractions.

There was a pause in the class as they mulled that one over. Then there
was a flutter of voices as the children talked to one another. I let them
discuss this for a minute or two.

TEACHER: Can someone paraphrase what Kyle said?   75

SHANTEA: I think he is saying that those pieces are fractions of
fractions, but what is that anyway?

MERYL: There is $\frac{2}{3}$ on one side and $\frac{3}{4}$ on the other side.

GERALDO: Almost like $\frac{2}{3}$ of $\frac{3}{4}$, but that's not possible.

CECILIA: Yeah! No way could you have $\frac{2}{3}$ of $\frac{3}{4}$!   80

At this point I decided to introduce an idea that might ease the
struggle that the students were having. I used the example that Geraldo
and another student had posed, but I put the idea into a simple and
meaningful context.

TEACHER: Think about this. Someone gave me $\frac{3}{4}$ of a leftover candy bar. | 85
[*I draw a diagram on the board.*]

I ate $\frac{2}{3}$ of that for lunch. What part of the whole candy bar did I eat?

MAURICE: Two thirds of $\frac{3}{4}$. That's got to be $\frac{6}{12}$. Just put some lines here, and you can see the $\frac{6}{12}$. [*He adds two horizontal lines to my* | 90 *diagram and shades in a portion showing* $\frac{2}{3}$ *of* $\frac{3}{4}$.] And $\frac{6}{12}$ is the same as $\frac{1}{2}$.

FELICIA: He's right!

Mario said he saw the $\frac{2}{3}$ as two of the three pieces of the leftover candy bar (in the original diagram), which he could then see was half of the | 95 whole candy bar.

Students discussed this information until the idea was more comfortable for them. They returned to the original problem and decided that we could indeed find the area of the entire region by taking all the things that we had counted and adding them together. They added unlike | 100 denominators by using Olivia's picture and thinking about equivalent fractions as they worked through the numbers.

Sarita

At the end of class, Basimah was busy studying Olivia's picture on the board.

BASIMAH: You know, another way to look at this would be to extend   105
the picture, to show the missing parts of the pieces of pieces.
That way we could just see what they were. [*She extended the
original diagram as she had proposed.*] Then you know that the
pieces are twelfths, and you can count them the way you can
count the rest of the pieces.   110

She was absolutely right! I asked her why she hadn't shared that with
the class, and she said that she just now discovered it by looking at the
picture.

After class, I reflected on the students' method to solve the problem I
had posed. My goal is that the students, at some point, will develop an   115
arithmetic algorithm from their picture. When I examine the diagram,
I recognize a procedure based on subproducts, much like the basic
principle that underlies most common algorithms for multiplying multidigit whole numbers.

To multiply $2\frac{3}{4} \times 3\frac{2}{3}$, find the subproducts: 120

$2 \times 3 = 6$

$2 \times \frac{2}{3} = \frac{4}{3} = 1\frac{1}{3}$

$3 \times \frac{3}{4} = \frac{9}{4} = 2\frac{1}{4}$

$\frac{2}{3} \times \frac{3}{4} = \frac{6}{12}$

Then add all the parts:

$$6 + 1\frac{1}{3} + 2\frac{1}{4} + \frac{6}{12} = 10\frac{1}{12}$$

This works, and seems very clear. But the procedure presented in most middle-grade mathematics texts involves changing mixed numbers to improper fractions, multiplying, and then changing the answer back to a mixed number.

$$2\frac{3}{4} \times 3\frac{2}{3} =$$

$$\frac{11}{4} \times \frac{11}{3} =$$

$$\frac{121}{12} = 10\frac{1}{2}$$

When I looked for these numbers in the picture, I found them by drawing more lines so that I could transform everything into fourths and thirds. By making darker lines to keep straight what stood for 1, I could then see how the twelfths appear.

Now that I understand this better for myself, I still need to think through my goals for my students.

Making Meaning for Operations

What I want my students to understand about multiplication

Henry
GRADE 6, DECEMBER

"What is it you want your students to understand?" has been asked of   140
me so often over the two years that I've been in this professional development project, I now automatically ask the question of myself. This
represents a change, because I used to set my goals by thinking "these are
the things I want my students to be able to *do*"—not unlike trained seals.
My students could move numbers around and about; understanding was   145
expected to come as part of the package. However, I'm not sure I ever
knew exactly what I wanted them to understand. This is my attempt to
nail down a few ideas about multiplication.

1. *Multiplication does not always make things bigger.*

   Whole-number multiplication leaves students with some observations   150
and assumptions that do not hold water when decimals and fractions
float by. This is one big misconception.

2. *Multiplication is not just repeated addition.*

   The link between multiplication and addition seemed to make great
sense with whole-number problems, but multiplication is a great deal   155
more complex than this.

3. *What is the mystery of "times"?*

   Many of my students read 7 × 9 as "7 times 9" but have no idea what
that means. *Times* seems to be an unfathomable word to some of them.

4. *3 × 4 = 4 × 3, but are they the same?*   160

   So many of my students seem "answer-driven," and the notion that
multiplication is commutative makes good and easy sense to them. But
3 groups of 4 *is* different from 4 groups of 3.

{ o o o o }   { o o o }

{ o o o o }   { o o o }

{ o o o o }   { o o o }

                     { o o o }

5. *How do you translate a multiplication expression, and can you understand what it means?*

The expression 5×6 could be 5 groups of 6, or it could be 5 taken   170
6 times. This interchangeable nature stretches a bit too far when students attempt to make sense of $\frac{1}{2} \times \frac{1}{4}$. The idea of "$\frac{1}{2}$, taken $\frac{1}{4}$ of a time" is of little value. Thinking about "$\frac{1}{2}$ group of $\frac{1}{4}$" makes better sense, but this, too, is not easy to understand. Drawings and pictures can greatly help understanding, at least when they aren't causing more confusion. My   175
sense is that confusion in these areas—translating the multiplication equation into something understandable, and being able to represent that understanding in a picture form—is desirable, for without that confusion, students will not achieve that understanding. And I think that understanding this stuff is key to understanding multiplication itself.   180

6. *The numbers in a multiplication equation are connected to real things.*

I want my students to be aware that numbers don't always exist by themselves—they are useful representations of things, such as people, money, or objects. And they help us solve real-world problems. I have found that when students make the connection between realistic   185
problems and multiplication equations, the operation of multiplication becomes clearer, and many of the misconceptions that exist when dealing only with numbers pose no threat.

7. *Students should not be hypnotized by numbers.*

A student will work with a problem like $3\frac{1}{2} \times 3\frac{1}{2}$ and get an answer   190
such as 37, or perhaps $2\frac{1}{4}$. These answers are outrageously incorrect, but many times we become blinded while computing numbers and fail to think about what those numbers mean. I want my students to realize that $3\frac{1}{2} \times 3\frac{1}{2}$ can't possibly equal more than 4×4 or less than 3×3. Estimation is a useful tool.   195

Henry

8. *There is a real connection between multiplication and division.*

Students seem to recite automatically that multiplication and division are opposites, and leave it at that. But to truly understand that $10 \times \frac{1}{2} = 10 \div 2$ and to contend with other problems such as this, it seems necessary to dig a little deeper. And there's mathematical gold to be found here, for stuff like reciprocals and division of fractions can then been seen in a different way.

Since I am sure there are more important ideas about multiplication that I have not yet touched on, I will leave this unfinished.

200

C H A P T E R

7

Expanding ideas about division in the context of fractions

CASE 28	Who says that's not the right equation? My own experience vs. students' thinking	*Sarita, Grade 6, May*
CASE 29	Stretching elastic	*Selena, Grade 6, November*

The cases in chapter 7 present the work of two sixth-grade classes as they solve problems that their teachers identify as division of fractions. These cases provide us an opportunity to study division of fractions for ourselves, but they also return us to the themes of this seminar:

- What does it mean to model a situation with a piece of arithmetic?

- As we see the various number sentences that could represent a single situation, what do we learn about the operations?

- How are our ideas about the operations extended as we encounter new situations they might model?

Who says that's not the right equation?
My own experience vs. students' thinking

Sarita

GRADE 6, MAY

The students in my sixth-grade class have been solving fraction word
problems for several weeks. Today they were spread around the
classroom, working in groups of twos and threes. The directions were to
draw a picture to solve the problem, write a number sentence (equation)
that explains the problem, and show any computation. This was the   5
problem I gave them to solve:

? You are giving a party. You have 6 pints of ice cream for the
party. If you serve $\frac{3}{4}$ of a pint of ice cream to each guest, how
many guests can be served?

For the most part, the students didn't find this a difficult problem.   10
They drew pictures to represent the pints of ice cream and separated each
pint into 4 equal sections. They explained that every 3 sections was what
one person would receive, and that was equal to $\frac{3}{4}$. There was enough to
do that 8 times, so each variety would serve 8 people.

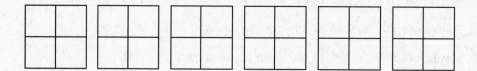

However, when they expressed this problem in a number sentence or   15
equation, the range of answers was interesting. I use the word *interesting*
because I am not sure whether the students are incorrect or whether they
just see things differently. Although I could understand the thinking
behind their equations, I didn't think that they were "correct." I had been

taught that equations have to match what is going on in the problem. In $\quad$ 20
my mind the students' equations were, though not necessarily wrong, not
quite correct, either.

I was trying to get the students to see that this was a division problem:
$6 \div \frac{3}{4} = 8$. Instead, they came up with the following equations and had
impressive reasoning to justify their thinking: $\quad$ 25

Equation	Justification
$24 \div 3 = 8$	There are 24 pieces, 3 pieces to a serving, 8 people can be served.
$8 \times \frac{3}{4} = 6$	8 servings of $\frac{3}{4}$ of a pint each gives you 6 whole pints.
$\frac{3}{4} + \frac{3}{4} + \frac{3}{4} + \frac{3}{4} +$ $\frac{3}{4} + \frac{3}{4} + \frac{3}{4} + \frac{3}{4} = 6$	$\frac{3}{4}$ each gives you 6 whole pints.
$6 - \frac{3}{4} - \frac{3}{4} - \frac{3}{4} - \frac{3}{4} -$ $\frac{3}{4} - \frac{3}{4} - \frac{3}{4} - \frac{3}{4} = 0$	Take $\frac{3}{4}$ pint for each serving. You can do this 8 times.

Students also presented some other equations along with those listed
above. Our routine is to leave all ideas out for discussion until the
students are sure that a particular idea doesn't make sense. Thus, the
following equations remained on the board even though I could not
accept their logic. $\quad$ 30

Sarita

Equation	Justification
$8 \div \frac{1}{4} = 6$	8 people were served, they had 6 pints, and the picture shows fourths.
$6 \div \frac{1}{4} = 8$	[*This was proposed in response to students who insisted that they couldn't accept the previous equation.*]
$24 \div \frac{3}{4} = 8$ or 6	There are 24 pieces altogether, and each serving is $\frac{3}{4}$ of a pint, so there are 6 pints or 8 servings (depending on what you are looking for).
$\frac{3}{4} \div 8 = 6$	$\frac{3}{4}$ pint is the serving, there are 6 pints of ice cream, so 8 servings.

These last few equations do not make sense mathematically, nor do the justifications help them make sense. In some ways these were the easy equations to dismiss. For the last one, I might be persuaded to help this student reexamine whole-number division, because the justification seems clear—it just doesn't go with the equation.

My dilemma is that the first set of equations do not feel "right" to me even though they make mathematical sense. The 24 ÷ 3 = 8 is disturbing. I see what the students mean, and I understand what they are doing; but these are whole numbers, and I think this is a fraction problem. Can it be both?

Where do I go from here? What do I do with my own thinking? What do I do to get the students to see this as a fraction division problem? Or do I? Who is confused, the students or me?

Stretching elastic

Selena

For a recent homework assignment, students were asked to solve a
problem by drawing a diagram and writing an equation. When they
arrived in mathematics class the next day, I placed them randomly in
groups of two or three for a discussion of how everyone in their group
solved the problem. Part of the homework asked for alternative solutions
to the problem, so students knew that listening to other people's ideas
would help them finish the worksheet. They also knew that I would
then select a group of students to come to the board to explain how they
solved the problem. This was the problem we were working on:

? A piece of elastic can be stretched to $5\frac{1}{2}$ times its original
length. When fully stretched, it is 33 meters long. What was
the elastic's original length?

The first group to come to the board solved the problem this way.
They drew a diagram showing the length of the stretched elastic.

MARCUS: This is the 33 meters. We want to put them in $5\frac{1}{2}$ groups.

The group proceeded to separate the 33 meters of elastic into sections
$5\frac{1}{2}$ meters long.

45

50

55

60

Before they could continue, hands all around the room flew into the air. Marcus called on Deena.

DEENA: I agree with the 6, but I disagree with what Marcus said.

TEACHER: What do you mean?

DEENA: I know what Marcus is doing, but I think he is all mixed up.   65

TEACHER: Can you say more about that?

I was not sure what Deena was thinking or what she was trying to articulate. It was difficult for her to express what she meant, but I wanted to give her the opportunity to explain her ideas.

DEENA: OK. The 6 is the answer. I know that because there are   70
           6 groups. Marcus said that they put the 33 meters into
           $5\frac{1}{2}$ groups, but they didn't do that.

TEACHER: Can someone tell us in other words what Deena is saying?

AMIR: I think Deena is saying that Marcus's group said one thing
           but did another. It doesn't really matter.   75

PATRICE: But if it doesn't matter, where did the 6 come from anyway?
           You don't know about the 6 until you solve the problem.

FRANCINE: [*She is Marcus's partner*] We didn't know about the 6 until we
           finished with the groups. I think Marcus meant to say that
           we kept counting $5\frac{1}{2}$ pieces, or meters, until we ran out of   80
           meters. When we finished, we had 6 as the answer.

TEACHER: Six what?

MARCUS: Six meters. I see what they mean though. I didn't make
           $5\frac{1}{2}$ groups; I made 6 groups of $5\frac{1}{2}$.

TEACHER: Can the problem be solved if we made $5\frac{1}{2}$ groups?   85

The students quickly discussed this question and began drawing new diagrams on their papers. Many were excited to think that I may have provided them with the alternative solution they were required to include on their homework papers.

I wondered if the students would be able to think about the commu-   90
tative property of $5\frac{1}{2}$ groups of 6 compared with 6 groups of $5\frac{1}{2}$. I also
wondered what would happen with the half when students tried to create

Selena

GRADE 6, NOVEMBER

$5\frac{1}{2}$ groups. How would they think about the half, and how would they express the half in their diagram?

When the noise settled to a calm hum, I called on another group. 95

SONIA: The answer will be the same no matter which way you do the problem. It doesn't matter because $6 \times 5\frac{1}{2}$ is the same as $5\frac{1}{2} \times 6$. Both of those are 33. I suppose you want a picture?

Sonia is one of my more proficient mathematics students. She tends to be quick to understand, quick to formulate an answer, and usually 100 not interested in drawing a diagram. However, I generally pretend I can accept nothing unless it can be proven with a diagram. So Sonia's group drew this on the board:

VICTOR: This picture shows $5\frac{1}{2}$ groups. There are 6 meters in each group except the last group. The last group only 105 has 3 meters in it, because it is a half a group.

TEACHER: What about an equation? [*Sonia wrote two equations on the board.*]

$$33 \div 5\frac{1}{2} = 6 \qquad\qquad 33 \div 6 = 5\frac{1}{2}$$

DAPHNE: We didn't do it that way, but I think it is the same thing. We 110 kept adding.

$$5\frac{1}{2} + 5\frac{1}{2} + 5\frac{1}{2} + 5\frac{1}{2} + 5\frac{1}{2} + 5\frac{1}{2} = 33$$

TEACHER: Is that the same, or is that different?

DAPHNE: It's a different way of doing the same thing.

ISAIAH: You could subtract also. Just keep doing subtraction until 115 you have zero. Oh! You would have to subtract six times!

$$33 - 5\frac{1}{2} - 5\frac{1}{2} - 5\frac{1}{2} - 5\frac{1}{2} - 5\frac{1}{2} - 5\frac{1}{2}$$

Chapter 7 135

The mathematics class was minutes from being over. Many of the students seemed to be thinking about the meaning of the operations of division and multiplication. I knew that there were many things I would like to have them discuss. Having a fraction in the problem did not seem to pose much of an obstacle; I wondered if that was because the fraction was a half, and many students had a special way of thinking about halves that did not always carry over to other fractions. In the days to come, I hope to test this theory.

But of course, the students could not let me rest on my laurels too long. In the last two minutes of class Philip confronted me with a new wrinkle.

PHILIP: When I do this the *real* way, I get a different answer: 6 r 3. [*He came to the board to show us.*] The 3 is half of 6. So the remainder is the half.

$$5\tfrac{1}{2} \overline{)33} \quad \begin{array}{c} 6 \text{ r } 3 \\ \underline{30} \\ 3 \end{array}$$

As everyone left, I thought to myself, "Half of what?" Now what do I do? Is this my lesson for tomorrow?

intriguing aspects of their students' thinking or learning, whereas researchers present ideas to support a theory or argument. Recently, however, the two approaches have moved closer together as researchers focus less on the ways individual children make sense of mathematics, and more on interactions in classroom environments and how they affect the learning process (Verschaffel, Greer, & De Corte, 2007). Taken together, the cases and the research illuminate much of the rough conceptual terrain students must travel as they navigate among the features of the mathematical landscape.

Our goal here is to weave these two genres together, so that each of many viewpoints contributes to the others. Having worked with a set of classroom narratives, we now turn to what various researchers say about how students come to understand addition, subtraction, multiplication, and division.

SECTION 1

Modeling addition and subtraction

Children arrive at school with an intuitive understanding of mathematics. They are able to model and solve word problems without ever being taught how, using a variety of strategies.

Children derive informal mathematical knowledge from all aspects of their world. Setting the table, counting objects to compare quantities with someone else, pooling collections of items, creating and distributing equal shares of a coveted snack—these and other everyday experiences form the basis of the mathematical understandings children bring with them from home as they enter school. As Piaget (1965) and Dewey (1938) show, a young child's understanding of her environment is action-based, and doing provides the substance for learning. The same is true when children encounter word problems for the first time. Without being shown anything formal about adding, subtracting, multiplying, or dividing, children act out the events described in the problems they see (Baroody & Standifer, 1993; Carpenter, Fennema, & Franke, 1996;

Carpenter, Fennema, Franke, & Empson, 1999; Carpenter & Moser, 1982; Carpenter, Moser, & Bebout, 1988; Empson, 2002a, 2002b; Empson, Junk, Dominguez, & Turner, 2005; Hiebert & Behr, 1988; Kamii & Warrington, 1999; Mack, 1993; Resnick & Singer, 1993; Smith, 2002; Verschaffel et al., 2007; Warrington, 2002; Wing & Beal, 2004).

Many of the actions children perform while solving addition and subtraction problems are derived from an understanding of counting and seem to develop along similar paths for most children. At first, students usually model all the quantities in a given problem by counting out objects to represent each distinct amount. Then they enact the problem situation by uniting or separating sets, finally counting the result. For example, when asked to solve the problem, "I have 6 rocks, and my friend gave me 8. How many do I have now?" children begin by directly modeling the action of the problem—putting out 6 objects to represent the first amount, 8 to represent the second, pushing the two sets together to form a single collection—then counting all the objects to get the total (Baroody & Standifer, 1993; Carpenter et al., 1999; Fuson, 1992, 2003; Gelman & Gallistel, 1978; Steffe, von Glasersfeld, Richards, & Cobb, 1983; Verschaffel et al., 2007).

What children do with the objects they use for modeling mathematics situations reflects their understanding of the structure of the situation. In the word problem described above, for example, the structure of addition is understood from physically joining quantities. Contexts that adults would recognize as simple subtraction might be interpreted in several ways by children—as separating amounts, as building on, as a comparison of parts to wholes, or as a comparison of unrelated quantities, depending on the context (Baroody & Standifer, 1993; Carpenter et al., 1996; Carpenter et al., 1999; Fuson, 1992, 2003; Mack, 1993, Verschaffel et al., 2007).

In a problem such as, "Electra has 14 rocks and loses 6 of them. How many does she have left?" many students assemble 14 items, remove 6, and count those remaining. Carpenter and colleagues (1996; 1999) call this action *separating from*, a procedure traditionally used to teach subtraction. In a problem such as, "My friend has 6 rocks. After she picked up others, she had 14. How many more did she collect?" students often put out 6 objects, add some more until the grand total of 14 is reached, then go back and count the number of things added. In this case the action performed is *building on* or *joining to*. With a problem in which one person has 14 rocks, another has 6, and the question is how many more the first person has, many students place 14 uniform objects in one row and

6 in a row underneath so everything is aligned, then count the number of items in the row of 14 that stick out beyond the objects in the row of 6. The action performed here is *comparing*, in which children use a matching strategy in order to identify the "extra." This is what Maya does in case 5 when trying to figure out how many stickers one girl has, knowing that the total is 14 and the girl's friend has 6 of them. (lines 221–225)

Although most conventionally schooled adults would probably call all the preceding situations "subtraction problems" and would represent each of them with the same equation, $14 - 6 = 8$, students often see these scenarios as qualitatively different from one another and solve each problem using a different action, as noted. The different actions performed highlight the distinct structures of various subtraction situations. Some researchers classify these structures as separate problem types (Baroody & Standifer, 1993; Carpenter et al., 1996; Carpenter et al., 1999; Fuson, 2003). Some students do too, as we see in case 4. There, Zenobia has trouble recognizing the similarity between a *missing part* problem (Max sees 3 blocks while his friend hides an unknown quantity of the 7 blocks he started with) and a *missing change* problem (Max has 3 blocks and finds an unknown amount, to end up with 7 blocks). To Zenobia, one problem does "not really" resemble the other in any way (line 27).

After children have modeled many situations in which they use objects to represent all of the amounts in an addition or subtraction problem, they eventually need to show only one of the quantities concretely. Initially students will represent the first quantity mentioned in a problem, counting up or back from that amount and keeping track of the number of counts made. Students later come to realize that it is easier to begin with the greater number and count on by the lesser number. In the case of the rock problems, while finding out how many rocks my friend and I have together if she has 6 and I have 8, someone might just count on from 8, putting up one finger to represent each of the rocks in the other person's portion, until six fingers are extended and six more numbers named. In the related subtraction scenario—my friend and I have 14 rocks together; if I have 6, how many does my friend have?—a student might start with 14 and count back 6, since this requires fewer steps than starting with 6 and counting up 8 (Carpenter et al., 1996; Fuson, 1992; Gelman & Gallistel, 1978; Verschaffel et al., 2007).

These counting up and counting back strategies mark a turning away from direct modeling in that they require a more abstract concept of number than the earlier "show all quantities" methods do. Children must understand the idea of *cardinality*—in other words, that a number name or symbol stands for a constant amount—as well as a position in the counting sequence. For instance, when counting rocks, 6 not only names the sixth number counted and stands for the sixth stone reckoned, but it also represents the 5 additional stones previously included in the count (Fuson, 1992). Latasha's diagram of the valentine stickers in case 5 illustrates this beautifully. The 6 stickers circled clearly include the previous 5, and the total of 14 stickers also depicts the addends embedded in the sum at the same time that the two amounts exist separately. In other words, as well as knowing that a number always contains the same quantity, children must also understand that numbers, in this case the 6 stickers belonging to one girl and the 8 belonging to the other, are parts of a larger whole as well as amounts in their own right.

Finally, children must be able to count from anywhere in a sequence and hold a double count, keeping track of both the number of items they start with and the number that gets added or separated (Fuson, 1992). In case 2, Denisha knows that in order to determine how many girls are in school when 2 out of 10 are absent, "You go down from 10 by 1, that's 9, and down 1 more, that's 8, so that's 2" (lines 206–207). This kindergartner is able to count backward correctly and monitor the number of counts made. She is still modeling the action in the problem but is doing it more abstractly than by putting out cubes to represent each child.

S E C T I O N 2

Numerical reasoning begins

As students grow beyond the need to represent all of the amounts and actions in problems, they no longer rely entirely upon counting to determine the results of joining or separating sets, beginning instead to reason numerically about the quantities involved.

When children are able to pay attention to how all the amounts in a problem are related to one another, when they understand which numbers represent parts and which designate wholes, they are able to select solution strategies that don't mimic the specific action of the problem. Understanding how parts and wholes are related to one another in addition and subtraction problems also allows children to combine and separate quantities more flexibly. Students often use strategies based on facts they already know when they get to this stage. They take apart numbers and recombine them to form new quantities that they find easy to work with (Fuson, 1992, 2003; Verschaffel et al., 2007). In case 5, for example, Cecile thinks about 6 + 8 as if it were 7 + 7, saying, "7 + 7 is easier for me to think about and that makes 14, so if I move 1 from one of the 7s to the other, I have 6 + 8 and that is 14" (lines 214–215). Cecile no longer needs to represent the specific amounts in the problem, nor does she rely upon counting when she needs to add.

Another example is found in *Building a System of Tens*, case 14. When asked to figure out how many of the original 37 pigeons remain after a dog scares away 19 of them, Fiona ignores the 7 in 37 and the 9 in 19, to subtract the resulting 10 from 30. She then subtracts 9 more from the remaining 20 to get 11, but is confused about what to do with the 7 she put aside in her first step. When her teacher asks whether those 7 pigeons left or stayed, Fiona knows to add the 7 back in to get the total of 18 (lines 233–237). Fiona, like Cecile, solves the problem by breaking the involved quantities into amounts that are easier to think about, considering carefully whether or not the 7 she deals with is embedded in the whole or in the part, and then reasons from there.

It is interesting that the growth from modeling all quantities and actions in a combining or separating problem to abstract reasoning with numbers is not a smooth or consistent transition for children. Some students appear to be at several levels simultaneously, able to count on when solving some problems, but needing to model directly when making sense of a scenario that involves something harder like separating, or maybe grouping, as shown by Bella's kindergartners in case 8, when counting legs on bunnies and eggs in baskets. These children are mostly still modeling every quantity in a problem and counting to get the total. At the same time, some are also grouping amounts in an array format, constructing 3 rows of 4 cubes each to represent the number of legs on three bunnies, which is a conventional representation for multiplication. They haven't begun to actually multiply and are still modeling all of the amounts directly, counting by ones to find their answers, but they are starting to expand their concept of addition to include the idea of combining equal groups.

Modeling multiplication and division

Although children come to an understanding of multiplication and division by modeling actions in a way similar to what they do for addition and subtraction, there are important and subtle differences.

One line of research suggests that children first encounter multiplication when having to combine several groups of the same size (Fischbein, Deri, Nello, & Marino, 1985; Greer, 1992; theory cited in Fuson, 2003; and in Verschaffel et al., 2007). Students again begin by modeling directly all the quantities and actions in a given problem. When trying to find out how many cans are in 3 six-packs of soda, for example, a child may first count out 6 objects, next count out 6 more, and then create a third group of 6, finally counting all to get a result. As students move beyond the need to show every item in a group of objects, they use a more abstract counting strategy, just as they do for addition and subtraction. However, instead of representing one amount and counting up or back from there, keeping track of the number of counts made, students might skip count to or back from a given number while tallying the number of counts (Carpenter et al., 1996; Carpenter et al., 1999; Verschaffel et al., 2007).

In the addition or subtraction situation, students are counting individual objects, whereas in the multiplication or division scenario, they are counting both distinct objects and groups of objects. Thus, when adding the number of soda cans in 3 six-packs, a student may start at 6, count up 6 more to get 12 sodas with the second six-pack, and then count up 6 more to get a total of 18. In this case, the student is counting every soda can in each six-pack, <u>6</u>, 7, 8, 9, 10, 11, <u>12</u>, 13, 14, 15, 16, 17, <u>18</u>. When multiplying, the child might put up one finger and count, "6," another and say "12," and a third finger, saying "18." In this latter case of skip counting, each of the three fingers raised represents a group of 6.

Later, according to this line of research, students are able to keep in mind all of the amounts in a multiplication or division problem and can break up numbers to use them flexibly (Baek, 1998; Carpenter et al., 1996; Fuson, 2003; Verschaffel et al., 2007). Examples of students making

160

165

170

175

180

sense of division at this level of abstraction, as well as a glimpse of how difficult it is to keep track of whether one is counting single objects or groups of objects when multiplying, are found in Janine's case 10. In this episode, three girls are trying to figure out how many packages containing 6 candy canes they would need so that each of 609 students could have one candy cane. Janine writes:

> Almost immediately the three decided that the problem had something to do with the 6 times tables—and that they had to go pretty far up the table to get to where they wanted to be. They started 6, 12, 18, 24, 30, and soon realized that there had to be a faster way. (p. 63, lines 261–264)

> [One student knew that 6 × 9 was 54, so 6 × 90 would be 540.] From 540 they decided that they had to add up by 6s to get to 609. . . . Letitia, after some thought, said that 540 + 10 more would equal 600. One of the others said that 540 + 10 is equal to 550 and not 600. Letitia struggled to explain. . . . She knew that 10 was important, but couldn't hold onto the idea that it wasn't 10 but 10 *groups of* 6 she was thinking about. (p. 63, lines 273–282)

Letitia works this through, and her group decides that 90 packages and 10 more packages would provide 600 candy canes. Another package would bring them to 606, but they recognize that they would need still another package to supply 609 students with candy. Here, as in addition and subtraction, the children use relationships they already know in making sense of multiplication and division situations; and they also demonstrate that "skip counting isn't a pure strategy," but is often used with addition when the most familiar sequences (2s, 3s, 5s, 10s) aren't employed or when knowledge of a specific progression of multiples, in this case 6s, gives out (Empson, personal communication, May 20, 2008).

Just as students come to understand multiplication as a way of counting groups or as a form of repeated addition, they may understand division as a form of repeated subtraction. In case 11, for instance, Vanessa divides 8 into 24 by writing $24 - 8 = 16$, $16 - 8 = 8$, $8 - 8 = 0$, and then writes 3 for the answer (lines 115–116). We can see, then, that some of these processes are similar to the modeling and counting strategies children use to figure out what addition and subtraction are.

However, multiplication and division are different from addition and subtraction in ways that aren't instantly apparent. Addition and subtraction situations involve numbers that count or measure amounts directly. Each number represents a set of something, a simple quantity. Problems are solved by joining, separating, finding missing parts, or comparing sets, and the result is a third amount of the same kind as the other two: 3 donuts plus 4 donuts gives you 7 donuts (Carpenter et al., 1999; Dienes and Golding [1966] as cited by Harel & Confrey, 1994; Fuson, 2003; Hiebert & Behr, 1988; Schwartz, 1988). Multiplication, though, frequently involves two factors that represent different kinds of things. Three bags each contain 4 donuts; how many donuts do I have? One factor is the number of sets, whereas the other is the number of items per set; both of these amounts must be tracked. The result is the quantity of donuts in all three bags, or in other words, the items contained in a set of sets (Greer, 1992; Harel & Confrey, 1994; Lamon, 2006; Thompson & Saldanha, 2003; Verschaffel et al., 2007).

To understand the idea of a set of sets, the child must be able to conceive of a collection as a *unit* (Harel & Confrey, 1994; Lamon, 2006; Thompson & Saldanha, 2003). In Bella's case 8, we see at least two children working with this idea as they represent the number of eggs there would be in three baskets, each containing 3 eggs.

> Jenna used the Unifix cubes. First she made a unit of 3 cubes and brought them over to show me. I asked her what she had, and she said that she had one basket.
>
> "Where are the other baskets?" I asked.
>
> "I haven't made them yet," she said, heading back to the table. Soon she was back again, this time with two units of 3.
>
> "How many baskets do you have now?" (p. 23, lines 495–501)

Jenna knows she has made two baskets and needs to make one more, which she goes off to do. Although she won't know how many eggs are in her three baskets until she counts them, she does realize that each group of 3 comprises a unit, namely one basket, and that each basket contains 3 items. Junior, on the other hand, is still building this idea. His model of the same problem consists of 3 orange cubes, 3 white cubes, and 3 yellow cubes. He knows he has three baskets, each containing 3 individual eggs, but when his teacher asks how many eggs he has in all, he says, "Three." Bella writes:

Junior showed me how he counted: Each unit of 3 was "one" to him. I took one unit and broke it apart. He counted them, "1, 2, 3," and agreed that they represented 3 eggs. I put them back together with the other two units of 3 and asked him how many eggs were there. Again, he said, "Three." I tried several ways to help him see that I wanted him to count the individual cubes, but it didn't help. He was unable to see the difference or sameness between cubes once they became a single unit of 3. (pp. 23–24, lines 521–527)

Whereas Jenna seems to understand the idea of a set of sets, Junior is still trying to figure out how one unit can be comprised of multiple items and yet maintain its identity as both a single entity and as a collection of entities.

To summarize, then, one line of the research literature suggests that children first come to understand multiplication as a way of counting groups, as just described, and then go on to construct other meanings for it later, as we shall see. Much of this research tries to define types of multiplication and division problems and examines student problem solving as it relates to those types. We will look at these ideas more closely in the next section of this essay. However, there is another group of researchers who find that students' ideas about multiplication and division develop not out of counting, but rather from experiences with *sharing*, in which equivalent portions must be created. It is in dealing out these "equal shares" that students come to understand ratio, multiplication, and division as inextricably related concepts, inherent in the same situations. They are doing this, in many cases, while still working on higher number counts and while sorting out addition and subtraction concepts (Confrey, 1995; Confrey & Harel, 1994; Empson, 2001; Empson et al., 2005; Lamon, 2006; Steffe, 2002; Thompson & Saldanha, 2003).

Consider, for example, the problem MaryAnn's fourth-grade students were working on in February (case 22): "I invited 8 people to my party (including me) and I only had 3 brownies. How much did each person get if they had fair shares?" (lines 28–30) Maribel still models directly the actions of the problem, using pictures to create and allocate her portions:

For example . . . she drew 8 faces for the 8 people at the party and drew 3 brownies which she cut into eighths. She then began distributing the pieces to the people. Each time she distributed 8 pieces, she crossed out the brownie they came from. After she finished distributing the pieces, she counted 295 them up. "They each get $\frac{3}{8}$," she wrote. (p. 86)

Maribel understands that this method results in equal groups, and she knows that the people in the problem have equivalent shares without having to count the portions. Although she uses counting to verify her solution, the actions she uses to solve the problem seem not to be rooted in counting nor, by extension, in repeated subtraction. Instead, they could derive from an independent action which Confrey and her colleagues call *splitting*, the basic structures of which are halving and doubling (Confrey, 1988, 1995; Confrey & Harel, 1994).

Although we don't see Maribel halving and doubling quantities in order to solve multiplication and division problems, thereby working out an understanding of what those operations mean, the DMI cases provide many examples of students doing just that. In *Building a System of Tens*, case 15, we see a majority of Eleanor's students halving and doubling to solve the equation 27 × 4. Stephan explains his process clearly:

> First way: I used my head only. I added 27 and 27 and I got 54, then I added 54 and 54 and I got the answer 108. I added 27 and 27 because I knew it was half of 4 × 27, so I put the two halves together and I got 108. (*Building a System of Tens*, p. 73, lines 29–32)

We later see the same class tackling division problems, again using a splitting strategy. In case 20, Mark has a bit of trouble keeping track of all the numbers he generates, but his classmates assist him. To divide 496 by 4 he explains:

Mark: First I'll take away 96 so I have 400. Then I'd do what equals 400, so it's 200, then half of that is 100, so it's 100. Then I have to put back the 96 and divide 90 but that's 50 and 40?

Jen: It's 45.

Mark: Oh yeah . . . so then I divide 45 in half and it's 22 and [*pause*] $\frac{1}{2}$. Then I go back to the 6. Six divided by 2 is 3 so it has to be . . . $1\frac{1}{2}$ . . . (*Building a System of Tens*, case 20, lines 115–123)

The teacher comments, "This idea that dividing is locked into splitting numbers in half seems to keep creeping into discussions as the days go

by. Is it a confusion in the way some children visualize division?" (BST, 330
case 19, lines 80–81) According to Confrey and a growing number of
researchers, it is not a confusion as much as it is a cognitive structure—an
idea in terms of which other ideas are organized—and it is a powerful
one, as both the cases and research suggest (Confrey, 1995; Confrey &
Harel, 1994; Empson, 2001; Empson et al., 2005; Lamon, 2006; Steffe, 2002; 335
Thompson & Saldanha, 2003).

Returning to the Making Meaning for Operations casebook, in case
11 we see that Georgia's students are still halving and doubling. Cory is
working on a problem in which someone is building bookshelves that
require 4 boards each; the person has 36 boards with which to work. Cory 340
reads the problem and then comments to his teacher:

> "I thought it was times." Then he reread the problem aloud.
> "See, that's why I changed it to divided by. If it was 4 divided
> by, I would probably use 2 first so it would be easier. First I
> would do 2 divided by 36, and that equals 28, and 2 divided 345
> by 28 equals 14 . . . Because I knew divided by is half of
> whatever the number is, like 2 divided by 100 is 50."
> (p. 56, lines, 140–145)

If we put aside the calculation error Cory's teacher helps him sort out
moments later, we notice that Cory sees multiplication and division as 350
interchangeable, and that his knowledge of both of them is developing
simultaneously, which supports Confrey's contention that multiplication,
division, and ratio co-evolve (Confrey, personal communication, February
3, 1997). We also notice that to Cory, division means splitting a number in
half, regardless of the structure of the problem. 355

S E C T I O N 4

Making meaning for multiplication and division

*As students sort out the various contexts that can be modeled by multiplication
and division, they continue to work on understanding the different types of units*

in these problems, deepening their knowledge of how the operations work and what they mean.

As mentioned earlier, one branch of the research literature (the one which suggests that children first come to understand multiplication as a form of repeated addition and division as repeated subtraction) examines student problem solving as it relates to the type of problems being explored. Two distinct types of multiplication situations have 360 been categorized, each of which is related to a division situation as well. We discuss the two types of multiplication and their related division separately, the same way this research typically examines them.

We have already described one type of multiplication, in which the two factors represent different kinds of things—one, the number of sets, 365 and the other, the number of items per set. Greer (1992) and Kouba and Franklin (1993) call this type of multiplication *asymmetrical*, because the multiplier and multiplicand play different roles and cannot be interchanged. As mentioned earlier, with the multiplication problem "3 bags, each containing 4 donuts; how many donuts do I have?" the two factors 370 can't be used in place of one another. Three bags containing 4 donuts each (4 + 4 + 4) is a different situation from 4 bags of 3 donuts each (3 + 3 + 3 + 3), even though both involve 12 donuts. If one person gets each bag, in the first case fewer people eat more donuts; in the second, more people eat fewer donuts. Because the two factors represent distinct types of units, 375 the related division situation can be defined in two ways (Fischbein et al., 1985; Greer, 1992; Kouba & Franklin, 1993; Thompson & Saldanha, 2003).

In one type of related division, known in the research literature as *partitive* and commonly called *dealing,* an amount is split evenly between a certain number of groups. An example of this sort of "equal sharing" 380 problem (Greer's term, 1992) might be this: "You have 12 donuts to share equitably among 3 people. How many could each person have?" The result is the number of items in each group or portion. In the other kind of related division problem, known as *quotitive* or *measure* and commonly called *grouping*, a quantity is split into shares of a certain size and the 385 result is the number of groups obtained: "You have 12 donuts. You want to make bags containing 3 donuts each. How many bags can you make?" Though both problems can be solved using the same division equation, $12 \div 3 = 4$, the solution to the first problem would be 4 donuts for each of 3 people, whereas the answer to the second would be 4 bags with 390 3 donuts in each.

Students usually represent and solve these two types of problems differently. For a quotitive situation like the one in which 12 donuts are packed in bags of 3, the number of donuts in each group is known and the number of groups is sought. To solve, students typically count out 12 objects and then put them in piles of 3 until they run out (Carpenter et al., 1996; Kouba & Franklin, 1993). Beyond the direct modeling stage, students might skip count (3, 6, 9, 12) to find out how many groups of 3 are in 12, or rely on their knowledge of multiplication facts (Carpenter et al., 1996; Fuson, 2003). Here, our classroom narratives contribute even greater detail to the research picture, since Georgia's students, in case 11, come up with other methods: repeatedly subtracting 3 from 12 until there isn't anything left to subtract from; adding 3 to itself to get 6 and then adding 6 to itself to get 12 (also documented in Verschaffel et al., 2007); setting up a chart showing that 1 bag contains 3 donuts, 2 bags contain 6, 3 bags contain 9, and 4 bags would contain 12. Though the first method could be based on counting, the last two might be considered *splitting* strategies, among possible interpretations.

When working on the partitive version of that same situation—"If 3 people are sharing 12 donuts, how many donuts does each get?"—students use several direct modeling methods. The most common is to select 12 items and then deal them one by one into 3 piles until they run out, counting the number in each group to get the answer. Another approach is to count out 12 objects to represent donuts, guess at a number that could go to each person, then deal out that many to see if any are left, and modify the initial guess if needed. A third method is not to count out the total to begin with, but simply to create 3 groups of an arbitrary size, keeping track of how many objects are used up, until the total of 12 is reached (Kouba & Franklin, 1993; Verschaffel et al., 2007). There are, of course, more abstract strategies as well—guessing an amount to skip count by and seeing if it reaches 12, then adjusting the guess accordingly so that 3 counts are obtained; or using known multiplication facts (Carpenter et al., 1996; Verschaffel et al., 2007).

The second type of multiplication described through this line of research is called *symmetrical* by Greer (1992) and by Kouba and Franklin (1993), because both factors play the same role, represent the same type of unit, and can be interchanged. One of the most common instances of symmetrical multiplication is area; the length of a rectangle might be 4 feet and the width 3 feet until you rotate the figure 90 degrees, when the length then becomes 3 feet and the width 4 feet. The same symmetry is true of the array model. If you have a box of chocolates arranged in

Making Meaning for Operations

3 rows and 4 columns, you can turn the box at a 90 degree angle and then have 4 rows and 3 columns. Another symmetrical form has been called *cross product* or *Cartesian product multiplication*, an example of which is this: "If you own 4 shirts and 3 pairs of pants, how many different outfits can you put together?" (Greer, 1992; Huinker, 2002; Verschaffel et al., 2007). 435

Because the factors are interchangeable in these scenarios, there is only one type of related division, in which a missing factor is determined. For example, if the area allotted for the rectangular third-grade garden is 12 square feet, and we've already put 3 feet of fence along one side, how much fence will we need for a side perpendicular to the first? Although the factors in a symmetrical multiplication problem are the same kind of unit (items of clothing, linear feet of fence), the result of such multiplication is a unit different from that of the factors. *Items of clothing* times *items of clothing* become *outfits*, and *linear feet* times *linear feet* become *square feet* (Greer, 1992; Kouba & Franklin, 1993; Verschaffel et al., 2007). 440 445

S E C T I O N 5

Encountering fractions in sharing situations

As students model and solve problems that involve sharing quantities equally, they encounter a new type of number: fractions.

There is much evidence to suggest that children explore sharing problems and begin to build fraction concepts before they reach school (Empson, 1999, 2002a, 2002b; Hunting & Davis, 1991; Hunting & Sharpley, 1988; Mack, 2002b; Piaget, 1965; Sophian, Garyantes, & Chang, 1997). Children encounter sharing situations early in their daily lives where they deal out a number of items and there is material remaining, as well as where the number of sharers is greater than the amount to be shared (Charles & Nason, 2002; Empson, 1999, 2002a, 2002b; Flores & Klein, 2005; Hunting & Davis, 1991; Lamon, 2006; Sophian et al., 1997). 450 455

An example of the first situation, in which children figure out what to do with the leftovers after dealing out items to share equally, is provided by Janie's case 21 in *Building a System of Tens*. There April divides 143 jelly beans among 8 students, finding that each person would get 17 candies with 7 left over. Janie writes:

> Then she came up with a way to divide up the 7 extra jelly beans. She took 4 of them and divided each in half, so each of the 8 kids got $\frac{1}{2}$. Then she had 3 left over, so she took 2 of those and divided them into fourths, so each kid got an additional $\frac{1}{4}$. Then she divided the last jelly bean into eighths, so each kid got another $\frac{1}{8}$. Now the question was, How much was $\frac{1}{2} + \frac{1}{4} + \frac{1}{8}$? (*Building a System of Tens*, pp. 98–99, lines 286–292)

April resolves this by drawing a circle showing $\frac{1}{2}$, $\frac{1}{4}$, and $\frac{1}{8}$ inside of it. From this she can tell there is $\frac{1}{8}$ of the circle unaccounted for, so each child would finally end up with $17\frac{7}{8}$ jelly beans. April, a fourth grader, obviously has much prior experience with dividing up quantities. She has already internalized the ideas that all the material needs to be used up and that everyone needs to have the same-sized share, two concepts that children don't automatically bring to partitioning tasks, as we shall see in Lori's first-grade class later on in this essay (Hunting & Davis, 1991; Hunting & Sharpley, 1988).

Children also encounter fractions in whole-number division contexts in which the number of people sharing exceeds the quantity of items to be shared. MaryAnn's students (cases 13 and 14) misread the problem $39 \div 5$ as "5 divided by 39" and then try to make sense of this latter statement. At first they see the two equations as synonymous, a phenomenon well represented in the research literature, and then go on to claim, "You can't divide a number that's lower by one that's higher" (p. 75, lines 35–36), an idea forged by years of experience with whole-number operations, and one that has also received research attention (Graeber & Baker, 1992; Verschaffel et al., 2007). Several months later when they revisit this problem at the next grade level, MaryAnn's students are able to visualize what 5 divided by 39 looks like by thinking about 5 candy bars shared among 39 people. Creating a context helps students see that "they would have to cut the 5 candy bars into little equal pieces" (p. 80, line 186); and "each person would only get a really small piece, not anywhere like a whole candy bar" (p. 81, lines 211–213).

Making Meaning for Operations

Although we see MaryAnn's students working to understand what fractions are and how they behave, much of the basic research about how children make sense of rational numbers has had a different focus. This work was done mostly in the 1980s and dealt predominantly with middle school and older children who spent many years in traditional classrooms, where memorizing the rules and procedures for solving computation problems formed the bulk of the mathematics program. The consequences of such instruction are visible in the research, which examines patterns of errors made by students, reflecting common "misconceptions." The overwhelming impression is of children who have lost the ability, even the desire, to make sense of the mathematics they are doing, a picture that stands in sharp contrast to some of the current research conducted in classrooms like MaryAnn's. So, with the caution that much of the early work about children and fractions focuses on what students can't do and don't know, rather than on what ideas are in place and which ones are still under construction, we turn now to what the literature says is hard for children to understand about fractions.

Even though addition and subtraction of fractions still involve joining, separating, and comparing amounts, just as for whole numbers, Carpenter found in some of his earlier work that students don't see fractions as quantities, "but see them as four separate whole numbers to be combined in some fashion" (Carpenter [1976] as cited by Vinner, Hershkowitz, & Bruckheimer, 1981). This finding was confirmed by the second and subsequent National Assessment of Educational Progress tests, in which students were asked to pick an estimate for $\frac{12}{13} + \frac{7}{8}$ from the choices 1, 2, 19, and 21. Most students chose the latter two, presumably combining either numerators or denominators together. Following whole-number addition procedures grown comfortable from years of rote usage, students lost the sense of $\frac{12}{13}$ and $\frac{7}{8}$ as quantities close to 1 (Behr, Wachsmuth, & Post, 1985), or perhaps they had never developed that sense to begin with.

Stafylidou and Vosniadou (2004), in their study of 200 Greek students ages 10 to 16, also found children thinking about fractions as if they consist of separate whole numbers that bear no relation to one another just as much of the previous research did (Carpenter [1976] as cited by Vinner et al., 1981; Behr, Wachsmuth, Post, & Lesh, 1984; Behr et al., 1985; Hartnett & Gelman, 1998; Post & Cramer, 2002). They point out that this lack of understanding emerges directly from a flawed generalization of the properties of counting numbers. Children assume that because you can determine the magnitude of a whole number compared to other whole numbers by its position in the counting sequence, the same will be true of fractions—but it isn't. With the counting or natural numbers, you always know where you are in the sequence because there is one unique number preceding and one following the number you consider. With rational numbers, there are an infinite number of quantities in between each count (Hartnett & Gelman, 1998; Smith, 2002; Sophian et al., 1997; Stafylidou & Vosniadou, 2004). For example, $\frac{5}{8}$ is between $\frac{1}{2}$ and $\frac{3}{4}$; $\frac{9}{16}$ is between $\frac{1}{2}$ and $\frac{5}{8}$; $\frac{17}{32}$ is between $\frac{1}{2}$ and $\frac{9}{16}$; …. Where the counting numbers are discrete, fractions are dense. While there is a least natural number to which you can compare all other natural numbers, there is no least fraction (Stafylidou & Vosniadou, 2004). In fact, the meaning of that smallest number expands when you consider the rationals. The unit no longer *necessarily* means a single entity. It can be a group of "several objects packaged as one" (Lamon, 2006), and can be conceived in many different ways at once.

An example Lamon likes to use is a case of soda. The unit is the whole case. You can think of it as $\frac{24}{24}$ if you are picturing each bottle, which is $\frac{1}{24}$ of the whole. Or, you can think of the case as 4 six-packs and the whole becomes $\frac{4}{4}$. Each six-pack is $\frac{1}{4}$ of the whole, or $\frac{6}{24}$ if you are thinking about the same $\frac{1}{4}$ being made up of single bottles. If you visualize the bottles placed in the 6-by-4 arrangement of the case and then split that array down the middle horizontally, you can see that $\frac{1}{2}$ of the unit consists of 12 bottles, or two six-packs. Now the whole can be expressed as $\frac{2}{2}$, of which 12 bottles make up $\frac{1}{2}$, which can be thought of as $\frac{12}{24}$ in bottles, or $\frac{2}{4}$ if you are thinking about the half in terms of six-packs. If you choose to split the case vertically, looking at each column of 4 sodas in the box, the whole is now represented by $\frac{6}{6}$, of which those 4 drinks comprise $\frac{1}{6}$ or $\frac{4}{24}$ if you are defining the case as bottles. In all of these situations the unit is still the same—a case of soda—but suddenly it seems a lot more complex (Lamon, 2002, 2006).

Thus we observe that when some of the ideas learned from years of counting are mapped onto all other sets of numbers, confusions can arise. As a consequence, some students have difficulty interpreting fractions as quantities. In fact, the entire idea of a quantity is challenged by fractions in that amounts are no longer "rendered when sets of things are counted. . . . One cannot count things to generate a fraction" (Hartnett & Gelman, 1998). However, sharing—an activity with which even young children have daily experience—does generate fractional amounts, as demonstrated in two of the cases we looked at earlier: Janie's class, where 143 jelly beans are shared by 8 people (*Building a System of Tens,* case 21) and MaryAnn's students, sharing 5 brownies among 39 people (this book, cases 13 and 14). In those classrooms, the students have already had some experience with fractions. In Lori's case 15, we encounter first graders attempting to make the transition from whole-number thinking to the kind of multiplicative reasoning required by fractions: many parts make up one set, or for every amount of *this* size, we have *that* amount. When asked how many brownies each of 4 friends would get if they were sharing 7, "many students came up with one of two different solutions. Either the students gave 1 brownie to each person and had 3 brownies left, or they gave 2 brownies to each person, giving 1 more brownie than was available" (lines 26–28). Both of these responses to equal sharing problems are well documented in the research literature (Hunting & Davis, 1991; Hunting & Sharpley, 1988; Lamon, 2006; Piaget, Inhelder, & Szeminska, 1960). For those children who could conceive of shattering the unit whole, the sharing strategy they used was halving (lines 50–58, 65–70) and repeated halving (lines 71–85), which confirms the masses of research literature that document the importance of one-half in children's developing conception of fraction quantities, equivalencies, and comparisons (Callingham & Watson; 2004; Confrey, 1995; Confrey & Empson, 2002a, 2002b; Empson et al., 2005; Harel, 1994; Moss & Case, 2002; Piaget et al., 1960; Reys et al., 1999; Spinillo & Bryant, 1991). The fact that most of Lori's students gave each sharer "an equal *number* of pieces, but not necessarily an equal *amount* of brownies" (lines 91–92), points to the dominance that whole-number counting actions have over the children's conception of quantity.

It is not unusual for children to bring their informal knowledge of numbers to bear upon problem types they have never seen before. Their tendency with fractions is to split the units into fragments and to deal with each fragment as if it represents a whole number amount. Children can thus consider the number of pieces involved in a sharing task without ever having to understand that the amount of each piece is determined by the relationship between the parts and the whole (Kamii & Clark, 1995; Lamon 1996, 2002, 2006; Mack, 1993, 2002b). Even if Lori had chosen to ask initially, "How *much* of the brownies would each friend get?" rather

than "How *many* brownies?"—a question which actually demands a
whole-number response—the results would have been the same, for it
is clear that these first graders have yet to develop an understanding of
the unit as a set of sets which can be viewed as a simultaneous collection
of any configuration of parts. They are just beginning to be able to split
the whole while sharing, though several of them have yet to realize that
portions must be equivalent, discrete, and that all the material must be
used (Hunting & Davis, 1991; Hunting & Sharpley, 1988; Lamon, 2006).
Beyond that, they will have to be able to "reunitize" the whole—keeping
in mind the size of the individual pieces as they relate to the size of the
unit, as well as the connection between the number of pieces in the whole
and the size of each piece—while thinking relationally about how those
shares might compare to ones created by other possible partitionings,
since there is a variety of possibilities embedded in each item or set to be
shared (Lamon, 1996, 2002, 2006, 2007; Steffe , 2002; Tzur, 1999).

S E C T I O N **6**

Understanding fractional amounts

When students begin to operate on fractions and other rational numbers, they
need to perceive these new numbers as quantities in order to make sense of what
fractions mean.

Being able to think about "how much?" instead of "how many?" while
fracturing the whole to form composite units represents "an important
conceptual leap . . . between additive and multiplicative reasoning"
(Lamon, 1996) because it implies the idea of comparison, which is what
a fraction is. The value of a fraction is defined by comparing the two
numbers that compose it. "It tells you how much you have relative to
the unit," the meaning of which changes with each context (Lamon,
2006). One-half is 2 out of 4 six-packs, if using a part-to-whole interpretation of fractions; or 2 boys for every 4 girls, if ratios are considered;
or the amount someone gets if sharing one thing with another person,
or 5 things with a total of 10 people, when the fraction is acting like a

610

615

620

625

630

635

quotient; or the size of the photograph you get if you shrink the original 50 percent, where the fraction behaves as an operator; or the part of a foot something that measures 6 inches in length is, when considering fractions in a measurement context (Kieren cited in Lamon, 2001). If the unit in question comprises two items, half of this whole is one item. One-third of this same set is two-thirds of one item. Three-fourths of one item in a two item whole is three-eighths of the whole set. It is no wonder that a deep understanding of fraction concepts takes years to develop (Behr et al., 1984, Lamon, 2006, 2007; Lappan & Even, 2002; Reys et al., 1999).

The key to developing a robust understanding of fractions—what they are and how they behave—lies in understanding the idea of equivalence, which arises naturally in many problem contexts. Smith (2002) sees it when children are engaged in repeated halving. Steencken and Maher's students deal with equivalence as they are engaged in deciding which of two fractions is greater and by how much (2002). Lamon (1996, 2001, 2002, 2006) demonstrates that fraction equivalence is embedded in the idea of looking at the whole as different simultaneous configurations and recognizing how each is related to the others, as illustrated with the case of sodas in the previous section of this essay. Empson's students (2002b) encounter the idea of equivalence when they arrive at with several different answers to the same equal sharing problem. MaryAnn's fourth graders (case 22) did the same while working on a two-part brownie-sharing problem: 8 children first share 3 brownies, and then share 2 more that are excavated from the bottom of the cookie jar. Some of the answers they obtained for this problem were $\frac{5}{8}$, $\frac{2}{4} + \frac{1}{8}$, $\frac{1}{4} + \frac{3}{8}$, and $\frac{1}{2} + \frac{1}{8}$. MaryAnn wonders if her students know that these expressions all stand for the same amount, suggesting that an understanding of equivalence is not automatic when working on sharing problems that yield the same amounts.

Empson, Smith, and others maintain that both partitioning procedures, such as repeated halving, and the ways children choose to represent what they are doing as they create equal shares, are how they first begin to make sense of equivalent fractions (Cramer & Henry, 2002; Empson, 2002a, 2002b; Moss & Case, 2002; Smith, 2002). Children create fourths by cutting halves in half, and then notice that $\frac{1}{2}$ is the same as $\frac{2}{4}$ and that $\frac{1}{2} + \frac{1}{4} = \frac{3}{4}$, based on their diagrams (Empson, 1999; 2002a; Flores & Klein, 2005; Smith, 2002). The DMI cases seem to confirm this. April drew a picture to figure out that $\frac{1}{2} + \frac{1}{4} + \frac{1}{8} = \frac{7}{8}$ (*Building a System of*

Tens, case 21). In case 19 of this book, is how Macario supported his argument that $\frac{1}{4} = \frac{2}{8}$ and how Rabia proved that $\frac{2}{6} = \frac{1}{3}$.

It is clear then that equal-sharing problems can lead students to construct the idea of equivalent fractions, but not without a significant amount of discussion. Empson says, "The way teachers talk with students about the fractional amounts they have created is central to the development of children's fraction concepts" (2002a). Other researchers (Behr et al., 1984; Cramer & Henry, 2002; Kamii & Clark, 1995; Lamon 2006, 2007; Steencken & Maher, 2002) also attest to the number of experiences and conversations that are necessary before children are able to make sense of the idea that "two different fractions actually represented the same quantity" (Empson, 2002b). This understanding requires knowing that when the units being partitioned are equivalent, the resulting portions are comparable—a key concept in ordering fractions (Steencken & Maher, 2002). Specific procedures do not need to be committed to memory, and several researchers found that after a while, just by working with fraction equivalencies through equal-sharing problems, students were able to compare and order fractions of many different sizes, in spite of the difficulties usually encountered (Empson, 1999, 2001, 2002a, 2002b; Empson et al., 2005; Flores & Klein, 2005; Steencken & Maher, 2002).

The trouble students have with comparing and ordering fractions is known to all teachers and researchers, and some causes have already been implied in this essay. Children with years of experience in determining the value of a quantity by examining its position in the counting sequence are not going to be able to use that method to figure out the size of a fraction. Knowing that 5 comes after 2 and is therefore more than 2 does not help us compare $\frac{1}{5}$ and $\frac{1}{2}$. Similarly, $\frac{2}{5}$ cannot be deemed equivalent to $\frac{5}{8}$ simply because the difference between 2 and 5 is the same as the difference between 5 and 8. Nor can $\frac{3}{4}$ and $\frac{2}{3}$ be considered the same amount just because when you count back one from 4 you get 3 and when you count back one from 3 you get 2 (Post & Cramer, 2002). Moreover, the language used to discuss fraction relationships often triggers counting-based understandings of quantity that end up confusing children. When Post and Cramer asked students which fraction in a pair was more than the other, or which one was greater, students would often respond, "Do you mean the size of the piece or the number of pieces?" (Post & Cramer, 2002).

There are many studies about the strategies students use for determining which of a fraction pair is greater, and interestingly, most of them are illustrated by the cases in chapter 4 of this casebook. In Faith's case 17, Harry compares $\frac{1}{2}$ and $\frac{2}{3}$ by drawing a picture, which is the first approach children use to figure out how fractions relate to one another (Smith, 2002; Empson, 2002a, 2002b; Empson et al., 2005)—unless they are working with commercial manipulatives. Such materials offer the same type of physical modeling as drawing pictures, and they are easier for young children to deal with since the need for fine motor activity like cutting and drawing accurately is obviated (Behr et al., 1984; Cramer & Henry, 2002; Steencken & Maher, 2002). However, these commercial materials often don't encourage the same kind of deep understanding and thinking that making one's own representations does (Empson, 2002a, 2002b; Kamii & Clark, 1995). Harry draws two rectangles of the same size, one divided in half with a horizontal line segment, and the other in thirds. He shades in each of the amounts to be compared and can see that more is shaded in his picture of $\frac{2}{3}$, so he concludes that $\frac{2}{3} > \frac{1}{2}$.

Annie (in the same case 17) also draws a picture in order to compare $\frac{1}{2}$ and $\frac{2}{3}$. She draws two circles of identical size, partitioning one in half and the other in thirds. She colors in $\frac{1}{2}$ of one and $\frac{1}{3}$ of the other. Since she knows that $\frac{1}{3}$ is less than $\frac{1}{2}$, she concludes that $\frac{2}{3} > \frac{1}{2}$. This method is documented in the research literature (Behr et al., 1884; Cramer & Henry, 2002). In the same case, Gary uses a variation of Annie's method, forming mental images to compare $\frac{7}{8}$ and $\frac{3}{4}$, relying (like Annie) on a comparison of the amounts that aren't shaded, but also looking at the distance of each fraction from 1. He pictures two equivalent squares, one split into eighths with 7 eighths shaded, the other into fourths with 3 fourths shaded. As he explains it, "You need $\frac{1}{8}$ more to make $\frac{7}{8}$ [into] a whole, and $\frac{1}{4}$ more to make $\frac{3}{4}$ [into] a whole. Since $\frac{1}{8}$ is smaller than $\frac{1}{4}$, then $\frac{7}{8}$ is larger."

Whereas Harry, Annie, and Gary are using pictures, or a combination of pictures and numerical reasoning, Faith's student Chuck (same case 17) is focusing on the numerical comparison between the numerator and the denominator in each fraction. He knows that the ratio between the numerator and the denominator in $\frac{1}{2}$ is 1:2, and that he needs to maintain the same 1:2 ratio between numerator and denominator in the second amount to show that the two fractions are equivalent. This means, if the denominator is 3, the numerator would have to be $1\frac{1}{2}$. Instead, he has a ratio of 2:3 between numerator and denominator in $\frac{2}{3}$, and since $2 > 1\frac{1}{2}$, he knows that $\frac{2}{3} > \frac{1}{2}$. Chuck is reasoning proportionally about these two amounts, and knows that the value of a fraction is determined by the *relationship* between the two amounts that compose it.

When asked to generalize some rules for comparing fractions, the 755 fourth graders in case 17 are able to articulate several of the strategies that have been documented in the research literature. Ami's statement in that case, "when there's a 1 on top in both numbers, then the smaller denominator is bigger," implies an understanding of the inverse relationship between the number of pieces and their size (reported by 760 Behr et al., 1984; Lamon, 2006). There is proportional reasoning involved in knowing that the more pieces you have within the whole, the smaller they will be (Sophian et al., 1997), and Empson (1999) has seen this kind of understanding as early as first grade. Rea's method (see Case 17) also involves some proportional reasoning. When comparing $\frac{2}{8}$ to $\frac{3}{6}$ 765 she knows that "3 is half of 6, but 2 isn't even close to 8," so by relating $\frac{2}{8}$ to $\frac{1}{2}$, a fraction she knows well, she is able to say that $\frac{3}{6}$ is larger. This strategy of comparing one of the fractions in a given pair to a different but common referent—like one whole, as Gary did above, or one-half, as Rea does here—is described by researchers, too (Behr et al., 1984; 770 Cramer & Henry, 2002; Lamon, 2006; Reys et al., 1999; Smith, 2002).

Bibiana, however, takes a totally different approach to determining whether $\frac{3}{4}$ is greater than $\frac{5}{6}$ (Nelly's case 18). She does draw some pictures like many of the students in chapter 4, shading in one 6-by-6 grid to show $\frac{3}{4}$ and another to show $\frac{5}{6}$. But then, as one of her classmates puts it, 775 Bibiana "translated the fourths and the sixths into twelfths." She looks at the $\frac{1}{4}$ that isn't shaded in one picture, which consists of 9 squares within the 36-square whole; then looks at the $\frac{1}{6}$ that isn't shaded in the other, which consists of 6 squares, and sees they are both made from chunks of 3 squares. One chunk of 3 would be $\frac{1}{12}$ of the whole. Therefore $\frac{1}{4}$ of 780 the whole would be made of 3 chunks with 3 squares in each, and $\frac{1}{6}$ would be made of 2 chunks of 3 squares. Because all of these portions can be defined in terms of the same unit, namely chunks of 3—or twelfths—they are easy to compare.

To Lamon, this is one of the core ideas in developing a deep enough 785 understanding of rational numbers to be able to use them in all their possible contexts. In addition to being able to visualize a fractional amount in several different ways simultaneously, according to which unit you choose to focus upon (like Bibiana does), it is also necessary to be able to compare numerators with denominators within fractions and 790 across them at the same time, and to see whether or not all these amounts are changing in relation to one another (as Chuck is beginning to do). The fact that an "estimated . . . 90% of students entering high school do not reason well enough to learn high school mathematics and science with understanding," and about the same percentage of adults don't reason proportionally either, suggests that this kind of multiplicative thinking does not "occur spontaneously" and must be taught (Lamon, 2006). The sort of teaching Lamon has in mind is exactly what is going on in the classrooms described in the cases. There is much research evidence which shows that building on students' informal knowledge of fractions by using problem situations drawn from daily experience will result in students who are able to understand what fractions are and how they behave, who can order fractions and operate upon them without ever being explicitly taught a formal algorithm (Empson 1999, 2001, 2002a, 2002b; Empson et al., 2005; Flores & Klein, 2005; Kamii & Warrrington, 1999; Lamon, 2001, 2006, 2007; Mack, 2002b; Pesek & Kirschner, 2002; Steencken & Maher, 2002; Warrington, 2002;).

We see Bibiana invent common denominators in case 18 while responding to a problem posed by her teacher. Without any instruction in specific procedures, Bibiana has created the idea she needs to answer the question "how much?"—an idea that is key to adding and subtracting fractional amounts. Jackson in MaryAnn's case 22 is working on that same idea. While figuring out how much brownie a person gets if the amount is $\frac{1}{4}$ of one, $\frac{1}{4}$ of another, and $\frac{1}{8}$ of a third, Jackson begins to fall into a whole-number rote memory trap, but then extricates himself as his understanding of the meaning of fractions kicks in. He explains:

> I was adding the $1 + 1 + 1$ [from the numerators] and it came to 3, but then I went to add the bottoms [$4 + 4 + 8$] and it didn't make sense. There's nothing here [in the problem] that's 16, and the numbers I was getting wouldn't match the brownies. . . . I know the $\frac{1}{4}$ and $\frac{1}{4}$ make $\frac{1}{2}$, and then $\frac{1}{8}$. So . . . each person had a share of $\frac{1}{2}$ and $\frac{1}{8}$ (p. 93, lines 170–176).

By focusing on the quantities the fractions signify, Jackson realizes that his original approach to the problem—attempting to fit addition and subtraction of fractions into his existing models for whole-number computation—makes no sense, though it is a common occurrence among students to join and separate numerators with numerators and denominators with denominators (Behr et al.,1985; Carpenter et al., 1996; Hartnett & Gelman, 1998; Howard, 1991; Stafylidou & Vosniadou, 2004).

Jackson knows that $\frac{1}{4} + \frac{1}{4} = \frac{1}{2}$, but it is not clear whether or not he realizes that most of the time when we combine fractions, we add together numbers which are expressed as parts of the same-sized implied whole. In other words, when thinking about $\frac{1}{2} + \frac{1}{8}$, we assume that both portions have come from brownies of equivalent size. Since the $\frac{1}{2}$ and the $\frac{1}{8}$ are defined relative to the same whole, they can therefore be understood as $\frac{4}{8} + \frac{1}{8}$. This idea of comprehending what the unit is—of knowing that when you add $\frac{1}{2}$ of something to $\frac{1}{8}$ of something, you are putting together quantities that are understood in relation to a third amount, the whole or unit—is difficult for children to grasp, but it is the same idea that Nelly's students in case 18 illustrate when they draw their comparative wholes as collections of 36 small squares.

Addition and subtraction of fractions can be further complicated for children by the fact that in some familiar, real-life situations that deal with ratios, adding numerators or denominators together is appropriate. For example, batting averages are computed by adding all the season's hits and dividing them by all the times at bat. If you get 5 hits in 8 times at bat during your first game, and 1 hit in 6 times at bat during your second game, then you are batting 6 for 14, or about .429. Field-goal percentages in hockey, soccer, and basketball are figured the same way—the total goals made per total attempted shots over the cou 1991; Lamon, 2006).

S E C T I O N 7

Revising ideas for operations with fractions

As the domain of number expands beyond whole numbers and into fractions, the ideas children have about operations, especially multiplication and division, frequently need revision.

When students move beyond addition and subtraction and into multiplication and division of fractions, their whole-number

Making Meaning for Operations

interpretations of those operations, especially if they are based on

counting structures, need revision. Repeated addition, for example,
which makes sense when modeling multiplication of whole numbers,
or a whole number times a fractional amount, doesn't seem to work
as well for multiplying two numbers that are less than a whole. For
example, when children combine whole numbers or fractions more

than one whole time, the amounts they end up with are always
greater than those they started with. Repeated addition of two fractions,
though, is hard to comprehend. When considering $\frac{2}{10} \times \frac{1}{2}$ as repeated
addition, what does it mean to add $\frac{1}{2}$ to itself $\frac{2}{10}$ of a time? Students
need problem contexts that are meaningful, as well as situations

which help them see that multiplication no longer necessarily
results in a number greater than either of the quantities operated upon
(Hiebert & Behr, 1988; Lamon, 2006; Mack, 2002a; Thompson &
Saldanha, 2003).

    Several researchers suggest that an area model works well for

illustrating multiplication of fractions, but that students first need to
understand this model in connection with whole-number multiplication
(Graeber and Campbell, 1993; Huinker, 2002; Mack, 2002a; Reys et al.,
1999). Even with lots of previous whole-number experience, students
still have to work hard to make sense of how to compute the area of a

rectangle with sides whose lengths include fractions. Sarita's students
in case 26, for instance, have found the areas of countless rectangles
with whole-number dimensions, but when determining the area of a
rectangle that has a width of $2\frac{3}{4}$ and the length of $3\frac{2}{3}$, it takes a while
for them to realize that they "could indeed find the area of the entire

region by taking all the things that [they] had counted," namely
$2\frac{3}{4}$ rows of $3\frac{2}{3}$ units each, "and adding them together" (p. 123,
lines 182–183).

    When children encounter division of fractions, their whole-number
notions of that operation are also challenged. A number can now be

divided by a greater number—contrary to what many students
believe is possible, until they are shown contexts in which this would
make sense, as, for example, when $\frac{1}{2}$ of a pizza is shared by 4 people
(Graeber & Campbell, 1993; Graeber & Tanenhaus, 1993; Sinicrope,
Mick, & Kolb, 2002; Warrington, 2002). Another conception about

division that needs revising when dealing with fractions is the idea
that division always "makes things smaller." In fact, the opposite is

now true if the divisor is less than one but greater than 0, as in the problem Sarita gave her sixth graders in case 28:

> You are giving a party. You have 6 pints of ice cream for the party. If you serve $\frac{3}{4}$ of a pint of ice cream to each guest, how many guests can be served?

In this case, the answer is actually more than either of the numbers operated upon.

None of Sarita's students represent what's happening in the ice-cream problem with a division of fractions equation—an outcome that puzzles their teacher. The students base their choice of operation on what they perceive the mathematical structure of the situation to be, rather than on the type or size of the numbers used, as the children in research studies often do. For example, one of Sarita's pupils took the 6 pints of ice cream and split them into 4 fourths each. That created "24 pieces, 3 pieces to a serving, 8 people can be served" (p. 131). The action performed by this student was grouping the 24 pieces by 3s, a division procedure, described by the equation 24 ÷ 3 = 8.

By contrast, children in numerous studies of classrooms in which computation procedures were the focus of instruction chose operations for problem solving based on the size or type of the numbers involved, instead of on the situation being modeled by the problem (Greer, 1987; 1992; Bell, Fischbein, & Greer, 1984; Bell, Swan, & Taylor,1981; Fischbein et a1., 1985). For instance, in one study when two problems with exactly the same mathematical structure but with different types of numbers were given, 12- and 13-year-olds picked multiplication to solve one and division to solve the other (Ekenstam and Greger [1983] as cited by Greer, 1992). The first problem, which they solved by multiplication, asked how much 5 kg of cheese cost if 1 kg costs 28 kroner. The second problem, which they solved by division, was essentially the same: How much would 0.923 kg of cheese cost if 1 kg costs 27.5 kroner? "It seems clear that the choice of division for the second problem is based on the realization that the answer will be less than 27.50, combined with the belief that multiplication always makes bigger, and division smaller" (Greer, 1992, p. 288).

Making Meaning for Operations

Conclusion

Although the vignette above and some of the other research described in this essay was conducted with children whose school mathematics experiences emphasized mastery of computation rather than making sense of number and operations, much of the research being done now focuses on classrooms like those described in the cases, where students are presented with problems to interpret and model in ways that make sense to them. In fact, the work of the educational researcher and that of the classroom teacher are moving closer together.

We read now of teachers engaged in "action research," studying how their students make sense of mathematics, often in collaboration with a college education program, or we read of researchers engaged in "teaching experiments," collaborating with public schools to see if the ideas for improved instruction emerging from the university are applicable and transferable to real classrooms (Adams & Sharp, 2006; Empson, 2001; Empson et al., 2005; Flores & Klein, 2005; Gomez, 2002; Lamon, 2002; Steencken & Maher, 2002). Teachers appear as guest lecturers in university courses, while education professors are teaching fifth-grade mathematics (Adams & Sharp, 2006). The merging of effort between the research community and public school teachers was signaled at the turn of the millennium by the publication of books with titles like *Putting Research into Practice in the Elementary Grades* (Chambers, 2002), in which researchers managed to maintain a separate identity and to offer the fruit of their independent labors to anyone interested. The newer efforts by NCTM, like the series *Teachers Engaged in Research: Inquiry into Mathematics Classrooms* (Mewborn, 2006), allow elementary and middle school teachers to publish their own studies, with the help of mentoring professors who use the information they glean from being in classrooms to help identify areas for further study. We also see educational researchers presenting experimental teaching protocols, problem sets, activities, and even fully developed curricula for teachers to use (Cramer & Henry, 2002; Lamon, 2006; Moss & Case, 2002; Vanhille & Baroody, 2002). These are often accompanied by brief classroom examples or narratives that sometimes read very much like the cases in this book, which are intended to help teachers anticipate the types of learning that can emerge with the use of these new materials, or which attest to their efficacy (Cramer & Henry, 2002; Lamon, 2006).

There are countless similarities between what teachers describe happening in their classrooms and the descriptions researchers give of their own work. If we look at all of it together—the classroom cases, and the formal or less formal educational research—the result is a richer and more nuanced picture than either discipline could produce alone. Together, they clearly depict the contexts being created to help students understand how real-life situations are represented by different types of numbers and operations. We are thus able to glimpse the complex process by which students internalize the mathematical structures of the problems they encounter. Though we may not fully understand this process, we can still recognize and support students as they move toward making meaning for the operations.

References

Adams, B., & Sharp, J. (2006). The impact of classroom research on student and teacher learning: Division of fractions. In C. W. Langrall (Ed.), *Teachers engaged in research: Inquiry into mathematics classrooms, grades 3–5* (pp. 13–32). Greenwich, CT: Information Age Publishers.

Baek, J. (1998). Children's invented algorithms for multidigit multiplication problems. In L. J. Morrow & M. J. Kenney (Eds.), *The teaching and learning of algorithms in school mathematics.* Reston, VA: NCTM.

Baroody, A. J., & Standifer, D. J. (1993). Addition and subtraction in the primary grades. In R. J. Jensen (Ed.), *Research ideas for the classroom, early childhood* (pp. 72–102). New York: Macmillan.

Behr, M., Wachsmuth, I., & Post, T. R. (1985). Construct a sum: A measure of children's understanding of fraction size. *Journal for Research in Mathematics Education, 16,* 120–131.

Behr, M., Wachsmuth, I., Post, T., & Lesh, R. (1984). Order and equivalence of rational numbers: A clinical teaching experiment. *Journal for Research in Mathematics Education, 15,* 323–341.

Bell, A., Fischbein, E., & Greer, B. (1984). Choice of operation in verbal arithmetic problems: The effects of number size, problem structure, and context. *Educational Studies in Mathematics, 15,* 129–147.

Bell, A., Swan, M., & Taylor, G. (1981). Choice of operations in verbal problems with decimal numbers. *Educational Studies in Mathematics, 12,* 399–420.

Callingham, R., & Watson, J. (2004). A developmental scale of mental computation with part-whole numbers. *Mathematics Education Research Journal, 16,* 69–86.

Carpenter, T. P, Fennema, E., & Franke, M. (1996). Cognitively guided instruction: A knowledge base for reform in primary mathematics instruction. *Elementary School Journal, 1,* 3–20.

Carpenter, T. P., Fennema, E., Franke, M. L., Levi, L., & Empson, S. (1999). *Children's mathematics: Cognitively guided instruction.* Portsmouth, NH: Heinemann.

Carpenter, T. P., & Moser, J. M. (1982). The development of addition and subtraction problem-solving skills. In T. P. Carpenter, J. M. Moser, & T. A. Romberg (Eds.), *Addition and subtraction: A cognitive perspective* (pp. 9–24). Hillsdale, NJ: Erlbaum.

Carpenter, T. P, Moser, J. M., & Bebout, H. C. (1988). Representation of addition and subtraction word problems. *Journal for Research in Mathematics Education, 19,* 345–357.

Chambers, D. L. (Ed.). (2002). *Putting research into practice in the elementary grades: Readings from journals of the National Council of Teachers of Mathematics.* Reston, VA: NCTM.

Charles, K., & Nason, R. (2002). Young children's partitioning strategies. *Educational Studies in Mathematics, 43,* 191–221.

Confrey, J. (1988). Multiplication and splitting: Their role in understanding exponential functions. *Proceedings of the 10th Annual Meeting of the North American Chapter of the International Group for the Psychology of Mathematics Education,* 250–259.

Confrey, J. (1995). Student voice in examining "splitting" as an approach to ratio, proportions, and fractions. In L. Meira & W. Carraher (Eds.), *Proceedings of the 19th International Conference for the Psychology of Mathematics Education, 1,* 3–29. Recife, Brazil: Universidade Federal do Pernambuco.

Confrey, J., & Harel, G. (1994). Introduction. In G. Harel & J. Confrey (Eds.), *The development of multiplicative reasoning in the learning of mathematics* (pp. vii–xxviii). Albany, NY: State University of New York Press.

Cramer, K., & Henry, A. (2002) Using manipulative models to build number sense for addition of fractions. In B. Litwiller & G. Bright (Eds.), *Making sense of fractions, ratios and proportions* (pp. 41–48). Reston, VA: NCTM.

Dewey, J. (1938). *Education and experience.* New York: Macmillan.

Empson, S. B. (1999). Equal sharing and shared meaning: The development of fraction concepts in a first-grade classroom. *Cognition and Instruction, 17*, 283–343.

Empson, S. (2001). Equal sharing and the roots of fraction equivalence. *Teaching Children Mathematics, 7*, 421–425.

Empson, S. (2002a). Organizing diversity in early fraction thinking. In B. Litwiller & G. Bright (Eds.), *Making sense of fractions, ratios and proportions* (pp. 31–39). Reston, VA: NCTM.

Empson, S. (2002b). Using sharing situations to help children learn fractions. In D.L. Chambers (Ed.), *Putting research into practice in the elementary grades: Readings from journals of the National Council of Teachers of Mathematics* (pp. 122–127). Reston, VA: NCTM.

Empson, S., Junk, D., Dominguez, H., and Turner, E. (2005). Fractions as the coordination of multiplicatively related quantities: A cross-sectional study of children's thinking. *Educational Studies in Mathematics, 63*, 1–28.

Fischbein, E., Deri, M., Nello, M. S., & Marino, M. S. (1985). The role of implicit models in solving verbal problems in multiplication and division. *Journal for Research in Mathematics Education, 16*, 3–17.

Flores, A., & Klein, E. (2005). From students' problem solving strategies to connections in fractions. *Teaching Children Mathematics, 11*, 452–457.

Fuson, K. C. (1992). Research on whole number addition and subtraction. In D. A. Grouws (Ed.), *Handbook of research on mathematics teaching and learning* (pp. 243–275). New York: Macmillan.

Fuson, K. C. (2003). Developing mathematical power in whole number operations. In J. W. Kilpatrick, G. Martin, and D. Schifter (Eds.), *A research companion to Principles and Standards for School Mathematics* (pp. 68–91). Reston, VA: NCTM.

Gelman, R., & Gallistel, C. R. (1978*). The child's understanding of number.* Cambridge, MA: Harvard University Press.

Gomez, C. (2002). Multiplicative reasoning: Developing students' shared meanings. In B. Litwiller & G. Bright (Eds.), *Making sense of fractions, ratios and proportions* (pp. 213–223). Reston, VA: NCTM.

Graeber, A. O., & Baker, K. M. (1992). Little into big is the way it always is. *Arithmetic Teacher, 37*, 18–21.

Graeber, A. O., & Campbell, P. F. (1993). Misconceptions about multiplication and division. *Arithmetic Teacher, 40,* 408–411.

Graeber, A. O., & Tanenhaus, E. (1993). Multiplication and division: From whole numbers to rational numbers. In D. T. Owens (Ed.), *Research ideas for the classroom, middle grades mathematics* (pp. 99–136). New York: Macmillan.

Greer, B. (1987). Nonconservation of multiplication and division involving decimals. *Journal for Research in Mathematics Education, 18,* 37–45.

Greer, B. (1992). Multiplication and division as models of situations. In D. A. Grouws (Ed.), *Handbook of research on mathematics teaching and learning* (pp. 276–295). New York: Macmillan.

Harel, G., & Confrey, J. (1994). *The development of multiplicative reasoning in the learning of mathematics.* Albany, NY: State University of New York Press.

Hartnett, P., & Gelman, R. (1998). Early understandings of numbers: Paths or barriers to the construction of new understandings? *Learning and Instruction, 8,* 341–374.

Hiebert, J. & Behr, M. (1988). Introduction. In J. Hiebert & M. Behr (Eds.), *Number concepts and operations in the middle grades* (pp. 1–18). Hillsdale, NJ and Reston, VA: Erlbaum & NCTM.

Howard, A. (1991). Addition of fractions—The unrecognized problem. *Mathematics Teacher, 84*(9), 710–713.

Huinker, D. (2002). Examining dimensions of fraction operation sense. In B. Litwiller & G. Bright (Eds.), *Making sense of fractions, ratios and proportions* (pp. 72–78). Reston, VA: NCTM.

Hunting, R. P., & Davis, G. E. (1991). Dimensions of young children's conceptions of the fraction. In R. P. Hunting & G. E Davis (Eds.), *Early fraction learning* (pp. 27–53). New York: Springer-Verlag.

Hunting, R. P., & Sharpley, C. F. (1988). Preschoolers' cognitions of fractional units. *British Journal of Educational Psychology, 58,* 172–183.

Kamii, C., & Clark, F. (1995). Equivalent fractions: Their difficulty and educational implications. *Journal of Mathematical Behavior, 14,* 365–378.

Kamii, C., & Warrington, M. A. (1999). Teaching fractions: Fostering children's own reasoning. In L. V. Stiff & F. R. Curcio (Eds.), *Developing mathematical reasoning in grades K–12* (pp. 82–92). Reston, VA: NCTM.

Kouba, V. L., & Franklin, K. (1993). Multiplication and division: Sense making and meaning. In R. J. Jensen (Ed.), *Research ideas for the classroom, early childhood* (pp. 103–126). New York: Macmillan.

Lamon, S. (1996). The development of unitizing: Its role in children's partitioning strategies. *Journal for Research in Mathematics Education, 27,* 170–193.

Lamon, S. (2001). Presenting and representing: From fractions to rational numbers. In A. Cuoco & F. R. Curcio (Eds.), *The roles of representation in school mathematics* (pp. 146–164). Reston, VA: NCTM.

Lamon, S. (2002). Part-whole comparisons with unitizing. In B. Litwiller & G. Bright (Eds.), *Making sense of fractions, ratios and proportions* (pp. 79–86). Reston, VA: NCTM.

Lamon, S. (2006). *Teaching fractions and ratios for understanding: Essential content knowledge and instructional strategies for teachers.* Mahwah, NJ: Lawrence Erlbaum Associates.

Lamon, S. (2007). Rational numbers and proportional reasoning, toward a theoretical framework for research. In F. K. Lester, Jr. (Ed.), *Second handbook of research on mathematics teaching and learning* (pp. 629–667). Charlotte, NC: Information Age Publishing.

Lappan, G., & Even, R. (2002). Similarity in the middle grades. In D. L. Chambers (Ed.), *Putting research into practice in the elementary grades: Readings from journals of the National Council of Teachers of Mathematics* (pp. 191–195). Reston, VA: NCTM.

Mack, N. (1993). Learning rational numbers with understanding: The case of informal knowledge. In T. P Carpenter, E. Fennema, & T. Romberg (Eds.), *Rational numbers: An integration of research* (pp. 85–105). Hillsdale, NJ: Erlbaum.

Mack, N. K. (2002a). Building a foundation for understanding the multiplication of fractions. In D. L. Chambers (Ed.), *Putting research into practice in the elementary grades: Readings from journals of the National Council of Teachers of Mathematics* (pp. 145–149). Reston, VA: NCTM.

Mack, N. K. (2002b). Making connections to understand fractions. In D. L. Chambers (Ed.), *Putting research into practice in the elementary grades: Readings from journals of the National Council of Teachers of Mathematics* (pp. 137–140). Reston, VA: NCTM.

Mewborn, D. (2006). *Teachers engaged in research: Inquiry into mathematics classrooms*. Greenwich, CT: Information Age Publishers.

Moss, J., & Case, R. (2002). Developing children's understanding of the rational numbers: A new model and an experimental curriculum. In J. Sowder & B. Schappelle (Eds.), *Lessons learned from research* (pp. 143–150). Reston, VA: NCTM.

Pesek, D., & Kirschner, D. (2002). Interference of instrumental instruction in subsequent relational learning. In J. Sowder & B. Schappelle (Eds.), *Lessons learned from research* (pp. 101–107). Reston, VA: NCTM.

Piaget, J. (1965). *The child's conception of the world*. Totowa, NJ: Littlefield, Adams.

Piaget, J., Inhelder, B., & Szeminska, A. (1960). *The child's conception of geometry*. London: Routledge & Kegan Paul.

Post, T., & Cramer, K. (2002). Children's strategies in ordering rational numbers. In D. L. Chambers (Ed.), *Putting research into practice in the elementary grades: Readings from journals of the National Council of Teachers of Mathematics* (pp. 141–144). Reston, VA: NCTM.

Resnick, L. B., & Singer, J. A. (1993). Protoquantitative origins of ratio reasoning. In T. Carpenter, E. Fennema, & T. Romberg (Eds.), *Rational numbers: An integration of research* (pp. 107–130). Hillsdale, NJ: Erlbaum.

Reys, B., Kim, O-K., & Bay, T. (1999). Establishing fraction benchmarks. *Mathematics Teaching in the Middle School, 8*, 520–522.

Schwartz, J. L. (1988). Intensive quantity and referent transforming arithmetic operations. In J. Hiebert & M. Behr. (Eds.), *Number concepts and operations in the middle grades* (pp. 41–52). Hillsdale, NJ: Erlbaum.

Sinicrope, R., Mick, H., & Kolb, J. R. (2002). Interpretations of fraction division. In B. Litwiller & G. Bright (Eds.), *Making sense of fractions, ratios and proportions*. (153–161). Reston, VA: NCTM.

Smith, J., III, (2002). The development of students' knowledge of fractions and ratios. In B. Litwiller & G. Bright (Eds.), *Making sense of fractions, ratios and proportions* (pp. 3–17). Reston, VA: NCTM.

Sophian, C., Garyantes, D., & Chang, D. (1997). When three is less than two: Early developments in children's understanding of fractional quantities. *Developmental Psychology, 33*, 731–744.

Spinillo, A., & Bryant, P. (1991). Children's proportional judgments: The importance of 'half.' *Child Development, 62*, 427-440.

Stafylidou, S. & Vosniadou, S. (2004). The development of students' understanding of the numerical value of fractions. *Learning and Instruction, 14,* 503–18.

Steencken, E. P., & Maher, C. A. (2002). Young children's growing understanding of fraction ideas. In B. Litwiller & G. Bright (Eds.), *Making sense of fractions, ratios and proportions* (pp. 49–99). Reston, VA: NCTM.

Steffe, L. P. (2002). A new hypothesis concerning children's fractional knowledge. *Journal of Mathematical Behavior, 20,* 267–307.

Steffe, L. P., von Glasersfeld, E., Richards, J., & Cobb, P. (1983). *Children's counting types: Philosophy, theory, and application.* New York: Praeger.

Thompson, P. W., and Saldanha, L. A. (2003). Fractions and multiplicative reasoning. In J. W. Kilpatrick, G. Martin, and D. Schifter (Eds.), *A research companion to Principles and Standards for School Mathematics* (pp. 95–112). Reston, VA: NCTM.

Tzur, R. (1999). An integrated study of children's construction of improper fractions and the teacher's role in promoting that learning. *Journal for Research in Mathematics Education, 30,* 390–416.

Vanhille, L. S., & Baroody, A. J. (2002). Fraction instruction that fosters multiplicative reasoning. In B. Litwiller & G. Bright (Eds.), *Making sense of fractions, ratios and proportions* (pp. 224–246). Reston, VA: NCTM.

Verschaffel, L., Greer, B., & De Corte, E. (2007). Whole number concepts and operations. In F. K. Lester, Jr. (Ed.), *Second handbook of research on mathematics teaching and learning* (pp. 557–628). Charlotte, NC: Information Age Publishing.

Vinner, S., Hershkowitz, R., & Bruckheimer, M. (1981). Some cognitive factors as causes of mistakes in the addition of fractions. *Journal for Research in Mathematics Education, 12*(1), 70–76.

Warrington, M. A. (2002). How children think about division with fractions. In D. L. Chambers (Ed.), *Putting research into practice in the elementary grades: Readings from journals of the National Council of Teachers of Mathematics* (pp. 150–154). Reston, VA: NCTM.

Wing, R. E., & Beal, C. R. (2004). Young children's judgments about the relative size of shared portions: The role of material type. *Mathematical Thinking and Learning, 6,* 1–14.